HERBCRAFT

A Complete Guide to the
Cultivation and Use
of Herbs Today

HERBCRAFT

NERYS PURCHON

PHOTOGRAPHY

ANDREW ELTON
NICK TRESSIDER
QUENTIN BACON

Blitz Editions

IMPORTANT NOTICE

This book contains information on a wide range of herbs that can be used medicinally. It is not intended as a medical reference book, but as a source of information. Before trying any herbal remedies, the reader is recommended to sample a small quantity first to establish whether there is any adverse or allergic reaction. Remember that some herbs which are beneficial in small doses can be harmful if taken to excess or for a long period. The reader is also advised not to attempt self-treatment for serious or long-term problems without consulting a qualified medical herbalist. Neither the author nor the publisher can be held responsible for any adverse reactions to the recipes, recommendations and instructions contained herein, and the use of any herb or derivative is entirely at the reader's own risk.

Published By Blitz Editions
an imprint of
Bookmart Limited
Registered Number 2372865
Trading as Bookmart Limited
Desford Road
Enderby
Leicester
LE9 5AD

First published in Australia and New Zealand in 1995 by Hodder Headline Australia Pty Limited,
(A member of the Hodder Headline Group)
10-16 South Street, Rydalmere NSW 2116

Produced by Hodder Headline Australia Pty Limited

ISBN 1 85605 308 3.

CREDITS

Our thanks to the following for supplying herbs:

Mother Earth Nursery, Kenthurst, NSW, Australia
Common Scents Cottage, Dural, NSW, Australia
Renaissance Herbs, Warnervale, NSW, Australia
Department of Agriculture, Windsor, NSW, Australia

The publisher would like to thank the following for photographic props:

Scott Milne, Wylies Pharmacy, Remuera, New Zealand: photograph on page 115
The Studio of Tableware Ltd, Mt Eden, New Zealand: photographs on pages 123, 133, 165, 191
Natural Body Care - 'Askew', Parnell, New Zealand: photograph on page 153
The Parquetry Floor from Ambiance Interiors, Parnell, New Zealand: photographs on pages 153, 187
L'image de Beauté, Parnell, New Zealand: photograph on page 161
Fionna Hill Floral Designer, Parnell, New Zealand: photograph on page 99
Beddingfields, Parnell, New Zealand: photograph on page 187
Palmers Gardenworld, Remuera, New Zealand: photograph on page 57

How well the skilful gardener drew

Of flowers and herbs this dial new!

Where, from above, the milder sun

Does through a fragrant zodiac run:

And, as it works, the industrious bee

Computes its time as well as we.

How could such sweet and wholesome hours

Be reckoned, but with herbs and flowers.

"THE GARDEN" BY ANDREW MARVELL

C O N T

ENTS

The wholesome sage, and lavender still gray,
Ranke smelling rue, and cummin good for eyes,
The roses, reigning in the pride of May,
Sharp hishop, good for green woundes remedies.
Fair marigolds, and bee alluring thyme,
Sweet marjoram, and daysies in their prime,
Cool violets, and Alpine growing still,
Embalmed balm, and cheerful galingale,
Dull popie, and drink quickning setual,
Veyne-healing verven, and head purging dill,
Sound savorie, and basil harti-hale,
Fat coleworts, and comforting parsline,
Colde lettuce, and refreshing rosemarie,
And whatso else of vertue, good or ill,
Grew in this garden, fetched from far away,
Of everyone, he takes and tastes at will.

"THE FATE OF THE BUTTERFLY" BY EDMUND SPENSER

This book is the result of a lifetime of involvement with herbs. In my childhood it was an unconscious involvement as it was so much a part of my life that I didn't question it. Herbs were not plants which grew in gardens but were gathered from (and often used in) the wild as the need for them arose. I have realised that, quite accidentally, the chapters in this book have followed the pattern of my life so far:

CHAPTER 1
Learning about the herbs in my childhood and using meadows and hillsides as my pharmacy.

CHAPTER 2
Moving to a beautiful valley in Western Australia and establishing terraced herb gardens, which flourished in the chocolate loam, pure air and river water.

CHAPTER 3
Using the herbs as medicines for people who came to the farm looking for natural remedies.

CHAPTER 4 AND 5
Beginning a skin and hair care cosmetic business using herbs and essential oils.

CHAPTER 6
Opening 'The Prancing Pony' restaurant where the emphasis was on herbs and fresh produce from the orchard and vegetable gardens.

My husband has always been an enthusiastic partner in every venture, allowing packs to be spread on his face, building workshops, and going out on the road as a cosmetic salesman. As 'head waiter' in the restaurant he kept everything flowing smoothly and now helps me to use a computer as well as fulfilling a host of other roles.

This book is the result of the support and generosity of all my family and friends.

CHAPTER ONE
HERB
KNOW HOW

I have a garden plot,
Wherein there wants nor hearbs, nor roots, nor flowers:
Flowers to smell, roots to eate, hearbs for the pot,
And dainty shelters when the welkin lowers:
Sweet smelling beds of lillies, and of roses,
Which rosemary banks and lavender encloses.

There growes the gilliefloure, the mynt, the dayzie
Both red and white, the blue-veyned violet;
The purple hyacinth, the spike to please thee,
The scarlet dyde carnation bleeding yet:
The sage, the savery, and sweet margerum,
Isop, tyme and eye-bright, good for the blinde and dumbe.

The pinke, the primrose, cowslip and daffadilly,
The hare-bell blue, the crimson cullumbine,
Sage, lettis, parsley, and the milke-whyte lilly,
The rose and speckled flowre cald sops-in-wine,
Fine pretty king-cups, and the yellow bootes,
That growes by rivers and by shallow brookes.

"THE AFFECTIONATE SHEPHERD" BY
RICHARD BARNFIELD

The herbs described in this section have been chosen for several reasons. Unlike many herb books, this book includes only herbs which can be grown in most gardens and these I have restricted to just under sixty. This may not seem many when you consider the hundreds of different herbs available on this earth, but you will discover that there is, in fact, a herb included for everything you need.

As with other things, quantity doesn't always mean quality. It is often better to use fewer herbs, with which you are totally familiar, than to confuse yourself with a large number which you never get to know and love.

My grandmother used herbs which grew in the meadows, by the river and at the roadside. I doubt whether she used even as many as I have included in this book but she was never at a loss when asked for help or advice. She would have been scornful and incredulous at the idea of buying herbs.

I have tried to use herbs which are reasonably available for you to grow yourself. It is sometimes quite a treasure hunt but, once you have established a connection with other herb growers, by placing an advertisement in your local paper or by looking in the telephone directory or alternative-lifestyle magazines, you will find it becomes easier to track down those elusive plants. The benefits to be derived from growing your own plants include knowing exactly how they were grown, dried and stored, and how old they are.

This book provides an easy way for you to learn about every aspect of herbs. You can begin your collection in a small way, enlarging it as you become more confident. After many years of teaching herbal medicine and the general use of herbs, I find that people feel more confident with herbs they've grown themselves, and use them more efficiently.

There is something magical about planting a seed, then several weeks or months later using the plant to make a skin cream, a healing ointment or a favourite dish in the kitchen. You also have the satisfaction of knowing the whole life history of that plant and being sure that you are indeed using the best.

They are all basically very safe herbs. Where care needs to be exercised there is a caution in the description. Herbs such as foxglove, aconite, arnica and many more have been omitted as they contain substances called alkaloids, some of which can be toxic in overdose. All herbs, however, need to be treated with respect. If a recipe or formula calls for one gram, two grams will not be better.

RECORD KEEPING

Once you start experimenting with herbs, you will want to remember what you did, so you can repeat it if the results are good and avoid doing it again when you make mistakes. A loose-leaf folder is handy, separated into sections for Growing, Medicinal, Cosmetic and Culinary. You can sub-divide these further, if you like. Culinary, for instance, might have smaller sections on Vitamins and Minerals, Teas and Cooking.

Every time you experiment, make careful notes about quantities, methods and results. This prevents those devastating times when you make something superb and can't remember what you used. I speak from bitter experience here. I have often cooked something wonderful which I was never able to repeat.

HOW PLANTS ARE NAMED

You are probably familiar with the use of common and Latin names for plants. Most people feel more at home using the common names, but with herbs, this can be a trap. I don't know how many plants there are bearing the common name of 'All Heal'. I know of at least five. Bruisewort and Colic Root are other examples of widely used names. I recently saw a punnet of plants in the nursery labelled Queen Anne's Lace, but when I looked at the Latin name it was something quite different from the herb used medicinally. Had I not known the Latin name I could have grown and used the plant with possible serious consequences.

So to avoid confusion in this book, I have used both, in this order:

COMMON NAME
Borage
Parsley
GENUS
Borago
Petroselinum
SPECIES
Officinalis
Crispum
FAMILY
Boraginaceae
Apiaceae

I have used the common name first in the headings, to help you find the herbs more easily. However, if you intend to make a serious study of herbs or use them in any of the many ways suggested in this book, you will need to know the genus and the species names, as these are the only accurate way of identifying plants. Buy your plants or seeds from reputable sources and only if the label carries the Latin name.

HOW TO USE THE LATIN NAMES

The different parts of a Latin name generally describe plants by the characteristics they have in common with other plants, such as stem construction, leaf shape or seed type.

A family is a group of plants having the same characteristics. Umbelliferae, for example, refers to a plant with hollow stems, with alternate, deeply divided leaves and with particular types of flowers. It includes parsley, angelica, anise and caraway.

A genus is a subdivision within a family, and species are the different varieties within the genus. In this way, gradually the description narrows down to something very specific, perhaps telling you that the leaves are serrated at the edge (serrata), or that the flowers are big (grandiflora).

The genus and species names are usually used together, such as *Borago officinalis*. There are sometimes disagreements among botanists about these relationships. You may see the name, shortened name or initial of the botanist who classified the plant added to the genus and species name, such as *Borago officinalis* (Linnaeus). The species name *officinalis* means that the plant is recognised in the pharmacopoeia as having medicinal value.

"There is something magical about planting a seed, then several weeks or months later using the plant to make a skin cream, a healing ointment or a favourite dish in the kitchen."

GLOSSARY OF BOTANICAL TERMS

ACID	Soil, water etc, with a pH level below 7.0, indicating the absence of lime
ACUMINATE	Coming gradually to a point
ACUTE	Coming sharply to a point
ALKALINE	Soil, water etc, with a pH above 7.0; can indicate the presence of lime
ALTERNATE	Leaves coming one after the other by turns, alternating
ANNUAL	Lasting or living for one year
ANTHER	Part of the flower that produces pollen
APEX	Tip or point
AXIL	The angle between leaf or branch and stem
AXILLARY	Growing from an axil
AXIS	The main stem or root, or the main line of growth
BIENNIAL	A plant that fruits in its second year and then dies
BILABIATE	Having two lips
BIPINNATE	Leaves which are doubly pinnate
BLADE	The flat or expanded part of a leaf or petal
BRACT	A small leaf that bears a flower in its axil
BULBIL	A small bud which may grow into an independent plant
CALYX	The outer covering of a flower; its separate petals are called sepals
CORDATE	Heart-shaped
COROLLA	The inner circle of petals
CORYMB	A flat-topped cluster of flowers where the stalks are different lengths. The outer flowers are the first to open
COTYLEDON	The first leaves produced by a seed, often different from the adult leaves
CRENATE	Having rounded teeth between sharp notches
DECIDUOUS	Plants which lose their leaves at the end of the growing season
DENTATE	Sharply toothed or notched
DISSECTED	Cut in fine segments
DORMANCY	The state of a plant which rests for a season; the growth above ground usually withers
ENTIRE	A petal or leaf with no teeth or indentations
EVERGREEN	Plants that retain their leaves all year
FILAMENT	The slender and threadlike stalk of a stamen
FILIFORM	Threadlike
FLORET	A tiny flower, usually part of an inflorescence
GLABROUS	Smooth and hairless
HARDY	A plant which can survive frosts; the opposite of tender
HEEL	A small twig or branch, carefully torn away from the main stem. This will root very readily

INFLORESCENCE	The flowering part of a plant; most generally used to describe a cluster of florets	PINNATIFID	Divided in a feathery fashion about halfway to the midrib
LANCEOLATE	Wide at the base, tapering to a point	PISTIL	The female reproductive organ of a flower
LINEAR	Long and very narrow with parallel sides	PROSTRATE	Growing along the ground
		RACEME	A lengthened cluster of flowers growing in pedicels along part of the peduncle
NODE	The part of a stem from where leaves and side shoots grow. Sometimes nodes are slightly thicker than the rest of the stem	RHIZOME	A fleshy stem, usually underground, which grows both roots and shoots (e.g. couch grass)
OBOVATE	Egg-shaped with the narrow end next to the base	ROSETTE	A circular arrangement of leaves growing from a centre
OBTUSE	Petals or leaves which are rounded or blunt	RUNNER	Similar to rhizome, but growing above the ground horizontally
OPPOSITE	Two leaves growing opposite to each other on a node	SEPAL	A leaf of the calyx
OVATE	Egg-shaped with the narrow end at the apex	SESSILE	Having no stalk
PALMATE	Hand-shaped	SPUR	A long, hollow, tubular projection from a sepal, containing nectar
PANICLE	A raceme whose branches are themselves racemes	STAMEN	The male, pollen-bearing organ of a flower
PEDICEL	The stalk of a single flower in a cluster	STIGMA	The tip of the pistil
PEDUNCLE	The stalk of an inflorescence or of a single flower	STIPULES	Small leaf-like appendages at the base of leaf stalks
PERENNIAL	A plant which lives for more than two years	TAPROOT	A strong, single main root growing vertically downwards
PETIOLE	A stalk	TRIFOLIATE	Having three leaves
PINNA	Single segment of a pinnate leaf	TUBER	The fleshy storage part of a rootstock
PINNATE	Shaped like a feather; two or more pinnae arranged on opposite sides of the petiole	UMBEL	A semi flat-topped cluster of florets where the pedicels grow from a common point (e.g. fennel)

AN A~Z OF HERBS

In reading these descriptions, you need to bear in mind that any description of height and colour can only be general.

There are many factors which determine the size and colour of a plant – the position in which it grows, the amount of water and fertiliser it receives and how happy it is. I have just measured a dandelion leaf in my garden and it is 38cm (15in) long. I also measured one from a dry piece of waste ground and it was 8cm (3in) long. The colours were different as well. Mine was a softer green and had a much more tender leaf. I'm not saying that the wild one is inferior, only that it makes identification much more difficult if you are not aware of these potential differences.

Alfalfa

Alfalfa

Medicago sativa
Family: Papilionaceae
Also known as lucerne or purple medick.

This is a most nutritious herb, a valuable source of complete protein and vitamin A. Each 100g (3½oz) of alfalfa contains about 8000 IU of vitamin A – more than apricots and about the same as beef. This vitamin is not affected to any great extent when the plant is dried. Alfalfa contains many other minerals and vitamins but has only recently been recognised as a valuable food for humans. Farmers have been feeding it to their stock for centuries without being aware that the animals were possibly eating better food than they were themselves. You can buy it in health food shops as seeds and in the supermarket as sprouts. It is a herb of great antiquity – I have heard that viable seed has been found in the pyramids.

This is a perennial legume, growing in compact form up to about 1m (3¼ft) in height. It has small, bright green, succulent leaves and tiny violet flowers in a cluster, followed by hairy, spirally twisted seed pods.

Grow it from seed to use as sprouts. It is resistant to frost and likes a moderate amount of water but, usually a field crop, it may not be very

Caution:
Alfalfa contains 20,000–40,000 IU per 100g (3½oz) of vitamin K1, which is a blood-clotting agent. This is normally a desirable vitamin as it reduces the risk of haemorrhage and seems to reduce blood pressure. However, if you are on medication to prevent blood clots forming, you should possibly avoid the use of this herb.

practical in the garden.

The whole herb is used medicinally to help stop bleeding, to benefit the kidneys and as a general tonic.

In the kitchen

Alfalfa sprouts go with cheese, eggs, rice and fish dishes. They can be used in soups, stews, vegetable dishes, cottage cheese blends, salads, sandwiches and as garnishes.

Aloe

There are two varieties: Aloe vera (short variety, also known as Barbados aloe or Curacao aloe) and Aloe arborescens (tall variety, also known as tree aloe)
Family: Liliaceae

This plant is amazingly drought resistant. Plants can survive a long, hot summer with no water at all. They look a bit sad and 'thin' by the end of the season but, as soon as the rains break, they become plump and juicy again. I am told that the aloe is planted on graves near Mecca. The Arabic name *saber* means patience, and patient this plant certainly is, as it waits on the graves of the faithful for resurrection day. It also waits in a dry corner of my garden for the autumn rain to fall.

Aloe vera grows straight from the soil to about 60cm (2ft), with no stem, as a rosette of thick, fleshy leaves, sometimes having pale creamy spots. The leaves are edged with spines, but they are not very sharp. The tall, annual flower head is a stalk bearing reddish-orange flowers.

Tree aloe grows tall – up to 3m (about 10ft) in warm, dry climates. The leaves are narrower and have sharper spines than Aloe vera. I have never found much

Aloe Vera

Aloe Arborescens

difference in the medicinal properties of the two aloes and use either or both depending on availability.

Grow plants from suckers in a sunny place or indoors (it doesn't like frosts) with little water.

The pulp inside the leaves is used to help the healing of wounds, minor burns, irritable rashes, stings and bites. It is also used as a mild laxative and is reputed to help ease the painful symptoms of arthritis.

In the kitchen

Aloe vera juice is sold as a gastrointestinal soother. You will find it in health food stores.

Aloe vera grown in a pot

Angelica

Angelica archangelica
Family: Apiaceae (Umbelliferae)
Also known as garden angelica.

Angelica was (and maybe still is!) considered one of the most important herbs for witches' brews. A well-known story tells of an old monk who dreamt that an angel visited him at a time when a dreadful plague was sweeping through Europe. The angel told him to use the herb to cure the plague-ridden people, hence the name angelica.

This is a large, hand-some, biennial plant growing to over 2m (6½ft). The stalk is round, grooved and hollow with a bluish cast. The lower leaves are very large with serrated edges, the upper leaves smaller. Large, round flower heads are borne in umbels in the second year. The florets are greenish-white and the seeds which follow are pale brown.

Grow it from fresh seed (the seeds are viable for a very short time, sometimes as little as 2 weeks) in a semi-shaded spot with plenty of water. It can tolerate frost.

The whole of this plant has a most delicious flavour for culinary use. It is used medicinally to aid digestion, to help coughs and as a diuretic.

In the kitchen

Angelica stem is good with stewed fruit or jellies, where it is a natural sweetener. It goes well in generous amounts in drinks, especially fruit juices, punches and liqueurs. It can also be used as a garnish.

Caution:
Do not use angelica if you are pregnant or are trying to become pregnant as it can bring on a period and thus cause miscarriage. It should also be avoided by diabetics as it has been known to raise blood sugar levels.

Anise

Anise

Pimpinella anisum
Family: Apiaceae (Umbelliferae)
Also known as aniseed or common anise.

This is the main flavouring for pernod, anisette and ouzo and has the reputation of being able to avert the evil eye. A dainty annual, of very similar appearance to caraway, it grows to about 60cm (2ft) high. The stem is ribbed and pithy, with kidney-shaped lower leaves and feathery leaflets of bright green above. Clumps of creamy white flowers are followed by grey-green, hairy, aromatic seeds, the part normally used.

The seeds need a warm climate to ripen but if this suits your garden, grow it from seed in a sunny place with a moderate amount of water.

It provides a general insect repellent to most plants and is especially good as a companion to asparagus, beans, broccoli, Brussels sprouts, cabbage, cauliflower, carrots, celery, cucumber, lettuce, parsnips, radishes, silverbeet, strawberries, tomatoes and zucchini.

It is used as an antiseptic and expectorant to ease the symptoms of whooping cough and to treat griping and wind. Helps to disguise the taste of less pleasant herbs.

In the kitchen

Use sparing amounts of the crushed or whole seed of anise to flavour cabbage, carrots, salads (you can use the leaves here too), tomato or vegetable juices, as well as biscuits, stewed fruit and liqueurs.

Basil

Ocimum basilicum
Family: Lamiaceae (Labiatae)
Also known as sweet basil or
garden basil.

Often called the king of all the herbs, probably from the Greek name, *basileus*, meaning king, basil must surely be one of the most popular and familiar herbs. In India, where it originated, it is revered as a herb sacred to Vishnu and Krishna. Some say that by carrying it in your pocket you will always attract money! The perfume of crushed basil certainly helps to sweeten and possibly disinfect germ-laden air.

The bushy, annual plant grows to about 30cm (1ft) high with opposite, smooth green leaves (normally the part used) and white or pale lilac flowers, occurring in whorls at the base of the leaves. The scent of the plant when bruised is very strong and clove-like.

Grow it from seed in a sunny, frost-free place or indoors, with moderate water. It is a good companion to apricot trees, asparagus, grapes or tomatoes, and repels aphis, flies, fruit moths and mosquitoes.

It is used as an antispasmodic and to soothe the stomach and treat griping and wind. It is also useful in aromatherapy.

In the kitchen

Use the leaves of this herb in moderate amounts with salads and vegetables. It is especially delicious with tomatoes. Also use in cheese dishes (including cottage cheese), curries, stews, salads and salad dressings, sandwiches and some fruit dishes. In hot dishes, it is best added towards the end of cooking.

Opal (red) basil growing amongst thyme and various other herbs

Bay

Bay

Laurus nobilis
Family: Lauraceae
Also known as sweet bay tree, true laurel and Roman laurel.

A tree which carries traditions in many cultures, the Greeks and Romans dedicated the bay to their gods of medicine. In ancient times, the leaves were made into wreaths to crown victors in sport, in literature and on the battlefield. The bay was grown to protect households against witches, warlocks and lightning strikes – woe betide the family if the bay tree died!

In warm climates the bay tree can grow to a height of about 18m (about 60ft) but in cold regions is much smaller, looking more like a big shrub. The bark is smooth with an olive-green colour. The leaves (the part used) are opposite, dark green, leathery and glossy. The flowers are highly perfumed, creamy-yellow clusters and are loved by bees.

Grow this from cuttings, which will strike more readily with bottom-heat. It likes a sunny spot with moderate water and will tolerate frost. It provides an indoor insect repellent, affecting mosquitoes and silverfish.

Medicinally, it is used as an astringent and to aid digestion and soothe the stomach.

In the kitchen

Bay leaves are a strongly flavoured herb and best added to hot meat and fish dishes, soups, stews and vegetables.

Bergamot

Monarda didyma
Family: Rutaceae
Also known as bee balm or Oswego tea.

The Oswego Indians of North America are said to have used this plant as a tea. During the Boston Tea Party in America, when British tea was boycotted, bergamot tea was drunk as a substitute. It is a most attractive spreading perennial, growing to about 60cm (2ft). The stem is square, stiff and hairy, with opposite, rough, serrated, greyish-green leaves. Scarlet flower heads at the end of the stem are supported by pale green leafy bracts. The whole plant has a delicious fragrance and is loved by bees.

Grow this from root division or runners in a semi-shaded position with moderate water. It will tolerate frost.

The flowers and leaves are used as a stimulant and for relief of griping and wind.

Bergamot

In the kitchen

The leaves and petals of bergamot combine well with salads and fruit dishes and may also be crystallised or used as a garnish.

Borage

Borago officinalis
Family: Boraginaceae
Also known as burrage.

The flowers and leaves are reputed to cool liquid in which they are steeped. Whether or not this is true, the flowers look lovely floated in a jug of water or lemonade and add a delicate cucumber flavour to the drink. Known as the 'herb of courage', the dainty blue flowers were embroidered by ladies on the jerkins of knights about to embark upon the crusades.

An annual which self-seeds so readily that it can take over the entire garden unless kept under control, borage grows to about 60cm (2ft) high. The whole plant is very hairy, the stems many-branched and hollow. The large, grey-green leaves are oval and pointed. The flower is exquisite, bright blue and starlike, with very prominent black anthers growing from the centre.

Grow it from seed in a sunny place with moderate water. The flowers hang down, so to see them at their best, plant them on a bank or wall where you can look up at them. They are a good companion to strawberries and generally increase other plants' resistance to disease.

The leaves and flowers are used for their lubricating and softening qualities, internally and externally, and their ability to cool the body down. Be careful, though, as the sharp hairs on the leaves and stems can cause throat and stomach problems. Any preparation used internally needs to be carefully strained.

In the kitchen

Borage flowers can be added generously to hot vegetable dishes, soups or stewed fruit. Cold, they enhance salads, fruit salads, drinks and dressings and can also be crystallised.

Borage growing in a herb garden

Calendula

Calendula

Calendula officinalis
Family: Asteraceae (Compositae)
Also known as marigold or pot marigold.

This is the herb to take as an ointment or tincture in your car or on expeditions of any sort. It is a fine healer for burns, cuts and lacerations. It helps to promote rapid healing without infection and with minimal scarring. Some believe that the hybridised calendula are less effective than the traditional, single variety but others declare them to be equivalent.

Calendula is an annual with bright flowers ranging from yellow to vivid orange. The alternate, slightly hairy, pale green, toothed leaves are very widely spaced. Don't confuse it with African or French marigolds, which are a little similar in appearance and are used as companion plants.

Grow it from seed in a sunny, frost-free place with moderate water. It will repel eelworm and is a good companion to beans, lettuce, potatoes, roses and tomatoes.

The leaves and flowers are used as an astringent and an antiseptic, helping to reduce bleeding and heal wounds, cuts and sores. It is good for sore nipples, ulcers, sprains and varicose veins. It also helps reduce inflammation and pain and stimulates bile production.

In the kitchen

Use calendula flower petals to flavour rice, salads and sandwiches, cottage cheese, fruit dishes and in crystallising.

Caraway

Carum carvi
Family: Apiaceae (Umbelliferae)
Also known as caraway seed.

One of the most ancient of all herbs and one of the best known today, records show that caraway has been used for more than 5000 years. Legend would have us believe that caraway seeds made into a potion and fed to straying husbands made them become faithful. Some pigeon-fanciers use the seed in the mash of homing pigeons, so maybe there is some truth in the old legend!

It is biennial, growing 40–60cm (about 1½–2ft) high, with a furrowed, hollow stem, finely cut, feathery leaves and umbels (flat-topped clusters) of white flowers in summer. The crescent-shaped, dark brown seeds (the part used) have five distinct ridges.

Grow it from seed in a sunny place with moderate water. It will tolerate frosts. In the garden, it repels aphis, flies, fruit moths, and indoors it repels mosquitoes.

The seeds are used to soothe griping and wind and as an expectorant.

In the kitchen

Use sparing amounts of caraway seed in vegetable or stewed fruit dishes, in baking, salads or soups.

Caraway

Catnep

Nepeta cataria
Family: Lamiaceae (Labiatae)
*Also known as catnip, catrup or
field balm.*

Even the most docile, aged and dignified cat goes quite silly when it smells bruised catnep. Very superior cats can be seen lying on their backs, flapping their paws in the air in ecstasy as they roll on the newly transplanted small herb, usually destroying it in the process. Catnep self-seeds so readily that you very rarely need to transplant it. 'If you set it, the cats will eat it. If you sow it, the cats won't know it.'

Catnep

Catnep is a perennial, medium-sized, shrubby plant growing to about 60cm (2ft) in height. The branching stems are square, erect and hairy, with pointed, scalloped-edged leaves. The whole plant is covered in a fine, soft, whitish down, particularly on the underside of the leaves. The flowers, whitish with lilac spots, grow in whorls on spikes from midsummer until winter.

Grow it from seeds, cuttings, root division, mounding or layering. It likes a sunny spot with moderate water and can tolerate frost.

Use all parts of the plant for repelling beetles indoors and medicinally to ease pain, relieve flatulence, relieve respiratory congestion and to cool, soothe and relax the body.

Be careful. In large doses, this herb is an emetic (induces vomiting). However, it is one of the best herbs for children if used as directed.

In the kitchen
Catnep leaves can be used as a flavouring when rubbed onto meat before cooking. Use the tender new shoots in salads.

Cayenne

Cayenne

Capsicum minimum
Family: Solanaceae
*Also known as bird pepper, capsicum,
chilli pepper, red pepper.*

Named from the Greek work *kapto*, meaning 'I bite', this pungent and fiery plant is a valuable source of vitamin C.

A perennial relative of capsicums, reaching 60–90cm (2–3ft) tall, its smooth stem branches out towards the top, with bright green, shiny leaves. The small white flowers have a drooping habit and grow either in groups of three or singly. The many-seeded long fruit changes from green to red as it ripens.

Grow it from seed in full sun away from frosts with moderate water. To grow the best fruit, it is best treated as an annual.

The fresh or dried fruit are used as a stimulant and to promote perspiration. It is used to treat cysts, cystitis, neuralgia and sore throats. However, overuse can cause damage to the digestive tract. Be very careful, too, when handling fresh chillies as the oil can create severe burns or blisters, especially if you touch your eyes with the juice on your hands. Wear rubber gloves to prepare a large quantity or use a fork to hold the chilli if just doing one or two.

In the kitchen
Commonly viewed more as a condiment (it is very hot) than a herb, cayenne, in sparing amounts, can provide a spike to all savoury dishes, dressings and vegetable juices, hot or cold.

Chamomile

Anthemis nobilis, also known as true or Roman chamomile, maythen or manzanilla.
Matricaria chamomilla, also known as wild or German chamomile.
Family: Asteraceae (Compositae)

Chamomile was one of the 'nine sacred herbs' of old England, along with mugwort, plantain, watercress, nettle, crab apple, fennel, chervil and an unknown ninth herb. Sometimes called 'herb of humility', it seems to like being walked on and one variety can be made into lawns, the most famous of which is at Buckingham Palace. There is an old English saying: 'The chamomile shall teach thee patience that rises best when trodden most upon'.

True chamomile is a low-growing creeping perennial, with alternate feathery leaves and small, daisy-like flowers with solid, cushion-like centres growing singly on erect stalks up to 30cm (1ft) tall. The whole plant has the fragrance of apples when bruised.

Wild chamomile is an annual, looking similar to true chamomile but coarser. The flowers have hollow centres, only one row of florets and are smaller than those of true chamomile. The plant is rather straggly and untidy-looking. It grows to a height of about 60cm (2ft). It has a less intense but still distinctive apple aroma.

Grow either from seed or true chamomile from runners or root division. It likes acid soil in semi-shade (although wild chamomile can take full sun) and is resistant to frost. Sometimes called 'herb doctor', it benefits sick or ailing plants growing near to it. Water your seedlings with weak antifungal chamomile tea to prevent 'damping off'. It also repels bacteria, cabbage worm and moths and is a good companion to cabbage.

The flowers of both types are used to relieve pain, calm spasms as well as stimulate appetite

German Chamomile

Roman Chamomile

Chamomile growing in a garden

and heal wounds. It is used to treat bruises, cystitis, earache, neuralgia, pain, sprains and swellings, nervous indigestion, tension headaches and sleeplessness. Particularly useful for children.

Be careful. Chamomiles can produce severe allergic reaction in some people. Treat this plant with care at first, especially if you know that you suffer from plant-related allergies.

In the kitchen

Chamomile is more commonly used as a tea than as a flavouring, although the flowers can be used to decorate salads or fruit dishes.

Chickweed

Stellaria media
Family: Caryophyllaceae
Also known as Starweed.

A common 'weed' which is found in gardens and waste ground throughout the temperate regions of the world. An annual with long, weak and sprawling branches which trail on the ground. The pale green ovate and pointed leaves have a long stalk at the lower parts of the plant and are stalkless towards the top. The stem is smooth except for a line of hairs running between sets of leaves, this line changing from one side to the other at each leaf joint. The chickweed flowers are small, white and star-shaped and occur on fairly long stalks.

Allow this herb to grow freely in your garden wherever it chooses – it doesn't become troublesome as it's very easy to pull up from the roots when ready to harvest and dry.

The whole plant can be used. There is no finer remedy for inflammation, ulcers, eczema, psoriasis and other itchy and/or inflamed skin

conditions. Internally it has a reputation as a remedy for rheumatism.

In the kitchen

The leaves are delicious eaten raw in salads or boiled as a vegetable. It is a good source of vitamin C and phosphorus.

Chives

Allium schoenoprasum
Family: Liliaceae
Also known as cives.
Another very ancient herb, there are records of its use by the Chinese dating back 5000 years.

A hardy perennial growing as a cluster of bulbs. The leaves are hollow, cylindrical, green and spearlike. A cluster of lavender florets grows like a pompom on a single stem. The whole plant rarely exceeds 20–30cm (8–12in) in height. If the flower head is nipped off, the leaves grow much more luxuriantly.

Grow it from seed or by root division in sun or indoors with moderate water. It will resist frost. Unless you are growing chives for their floral display, cut the flower stalks off as they appear or the plant becomes weakened. They are easy to grow, have very pretty flowers and are ideal for children to grow to begin their own herb gardens. They repel aphis, apple scab and fungus and are a good companion to apple trees, carrots, cucumber and tomatoes.

The leaves are used to aid digestion and as a general tonic.

In the kitchen

Use generous amounts of the chopped leaves of chives in cheese, egg, seafood, potato or vegetable dishes, sauces, soups, salads, dressings, vegetable juices or as a savoury garnish.

Comfrey

Symphytum officinale
Family: Boraginaceae
Also known as knitbone, knitback, boneset, bruisewort
or gum plant.

There is so much written about comfrey that it seems an insult to devote only a few lines to this herb. The myths and legends surrounding comfrey are many.

The rootes of comfrey, stamped, and the juice drunke with wine, helpeth those that spit bloud, and healeth all inward wounds and bruising. The same bruised and laide to in a manner of a plaister, doth heale all fresh and greene wounds, and are so glutinative, that it will sodder or glew togither meate that is chopt in peeces seething in a pot, and make it in one lumpe.

JOHN GERARD, THE HERBALL, 1597

Comfrey is a spreading, leafy perennial, dormant in winter, growing as tall as 90cm (3ft) under good conditions. The rootstock is very brittle and blackish on the outside, white and fleshy on the inside. The juice in the root is sticky. The stem is hollow, angular and very hairy. The leaves are hairy, long and pointed. They are very large at the base of the plant and decrease in size further up the stem. The stem ends in clusters of pale pink, pale yellow or pale mauve softly drooping flowers.

Grow it from root division in a sunny place with moderate water. Keep it under control or it can take over the garden. Comfrey is the only plant I know that will tolerate fresh manure and still thrive.

The root and leaves of comfrey are used for their anti-inflammatory, softening, lubricating, and wound-healing properties. They are used to treat arthritis, boils, bruises, sore nipples, wounds, cuts and sores, ulcers, sprains, stings and bites, and swellings.

There has recently been some concern that it might damage the stomach and liver, so it is now considered safest to use this herb externally only.

Comfrey

The root and leaves of comfrey are used for their anti-inflammatory, softening, lubricating, and wound-healing properties.

A comfrey plant

Coriander

Coriandrum sativum
Family: Apiaceae (Umbelliferae)
Also known as dizzicorn,
Chinese parsley or cilantro.

Coriander seems to have originated in the East, but the warm, spicy aroma also arouses visions of Mexican food and is a favourite culinary herb. In the Arabian stories, *The Thousand and One Nights*, coriander is said to have aphrodisiac qualities. It is also documented as having been used in love potions during the Middle Ages.

An annual, growing 30–60cm (1–2ft) high, the stem is many-branched and erect, bearing bright green leaves a little like parsley. The flowers are delicate umbels in shades ranging from palest pink to mauve, while the seeds turn from green to a pale beige colour as they ripen and take on a warm, aromatic, spicy odour.

Grow it from seed in a frost-free, sunny place with moderate water. It repels aphis, black fly, cabbage moth and cabbage worm and is a good companion to cabbage and carrots. The leaves and seeds are used for their antispasmodic and aromatic qualities and to soothe the stomach and relieve griping and wind.

In the kitchen
The seeds can be used in relishes and chutneys and even in sweet foods such as cakes, biscuits and pies. The leaves, stems and roots add a zesty flavour to curries, salads, casseroles and soups. The leaves also make an attractive garnish.

Coriander

Dandelion

Taraxacum officinale
Family: Asteraceae (Compositae)
Also known as blowball, swine's snout,
priest's crown or timetable.

Often called a 'royal herb', dandelion is a powerhouse of goodness. Through the ages, it has been revered as a 'cure-all', so think twice before you weed it out of your garden.

It is a perennial with a thick, juicy root, black on the outside and white inside. The pale green, hairless leaves are oblong and notched and rise directly out of the root. A single, smooth flower stem also rises from the root. It is hollow and ends in a single flower head with a collection of golden petals which turns into a white, downy, 'puffball' head of seeds. When snapped, the stem exudes a white 'milk'. It is often confused with other herbs but the single, hollow stem is a key identifier.

Dandelion

Grow it from seed in full sun with little water if you wish to cultivate it, but be careful. It can take over the garden and it is not usually too difficult to find wild stocks if you want to use this herb.

The root and leaves are used for their anti-inflammatory, cleansing properties. It has a laxative and diuretic effect and gently stimulates the liver and bile production. Dandelion helps to relieve toxic conditions such as joint inflammation, and is very valuable for its vitamin and mineral content.

In the kitchen
This extraordinary herb, often viewed as a weed, is high in many vitamins and minerals and the very young leaves are used in salads. Moderate amounts of the petals will brighten salads, too.

Dill

Anethum graveolens
Family: Apiaceae (Umbelliferae)
Also known as dill seed, benth, fructus anethi or dill weed.

Dill was once considered to be a protection against witches. Now better known to many mothers of 'colicky' babies for its ability to 'bring up the wind', it is a blessing to sore tummies. It is often confused with fennel as the leaves, seeds and flavour are a little similar. However, mistakes are not serious as both are very mild and have a similar action.

Dill

Dill is an annual, growing to a height of 30–60cm (1–2ft). The stem is smooth and upright. The leaves are similar in appearance to fennel, being bipinnate, but are a darker green and much smaller. The flowers are small and yellow, borne on flat umbels from midsummer onwards. The seeds, which succeed the flowers, are oval, flat, ribbed and light brown in colour.

Grow it from seed in a frost-free, sunny spot with moderate water. It repels cabbage moth and is a good companion to cabbage, celery and all varieties of tomatoes.

The leaves and seeds are used as an antispasmodic and diuretic and to soothe the stomach and relieve griping and wind. Particularly useful for babies.

In the kitchen

The seeds and leaves of dill can be used in moderate amounts in vegetable, egg, lamb and shellfish dishes, soups, cottage cheese, salads, sandwiches, pickles, dressings and vinegars.

Echinacea

Echinacea angustifolia, E. purpurea
Family: Asteraceae (Compositae)
Also known as purple coneflower, niggerhead, rudbeckia, black sampson.

Echinacea purpurea is a strong plant, growing to approximately 30–60cm (1–2ft tall), with wide leaves. It has large flowers with pink-purple petals which droop and a high central blackish cone. The root is medicinally the most important part of both varieties although the whole plant may also be used.

Echinacea angustifolia is shorter, has narrower leaves and the flower petals are purple and more upright.

Grow it from seed in a sunny position. It prefers not to be too wet and it is winter dormant.

Echinacea may be used as the whole plant, tincture or an extract. It has been my experience that a tincture is to be preferred as it begins to work in the mouth.

It is a remarkable herb, non-toxic and with no known adverse side effects. Use to increase the body's resistance to infections; improve recovery from viral, fungal and bacterial infections.

Echinacea

Elder

Sambucus nigra
Family: Caprifoliaceae
Also known as black, European or German elder.

It would be possible to fill a small book with folklore about the elder. Children and grandchildren are always impressed when told they need to ask permission from the Elder Mother before taking any part of her tree or she will punish them severely! It is said that if you make a cradle from elder wood, the fairies will steal your baby and leave a fairy baby in its place. I have never seen a fairy baby but I understand they are exceptionally ugly and very bad-tempered, so it really doesn't seem worth taking the risk.

It is a large bush or small tree, growing to about 6m (about 20ft) in the right conditions. The rough grey stems bear large leaves and large, creamy white umbels of sweet-smelling flowers, followed by drooping bunches of purple berries.

Grow it from cuttings in the sun with moderate water. It is frost-resistant and prefers a cool climate to fruit properly. It repels aphis and caterpillars.

Elder is useful for a mouthwash and gargle during inflammation.

The flowers are the most widely used part of the plant. They promote perspiration during feverish conditions such as colds and flu, particularly when combined with peppermint and yarrow. Used as an expectorant, diuretic and anti-inflammatory; also in healing creams and skin preparations for its soothing and softening action.

In the kitchen
Delicious fritters can be made by dipping the flower heads in a light batter. Deep-fry, then sprinkle with caster sugar.

Fennel

Foeniculum vulgare
Family: Apiaceae (Umbelliferae)
Also known as sweet or wild fennel.
Many of the ancient writers mention the slimming properties of fennel as it seems to be an appetite depressant. Chewing the seeds will keep hunger pangs at bay. Fennel is one of the 'nine sacred herbs' (see chamomile).

A most handsome perennial plant, graceful and feathery, fennel is an ornament to any garden. The strong, tubular, bright green stems grow to about 1–2m (3¼–6½ft). The threadlike leaves (like dill but much larger) grow from sheaths which surround the stem, and the flower heads, flat clusters of bright yellow florets, bloom from late spring onwards. The seeds are slightly curved and greyish-green in colour, becoming brown when dried.

Grow this from seed in the sun with little water, but be careful as it can take over the garden. It repels fleas, so use it on the pet's bed. Plant it away from beans, kohlrabi and tomatoes as it doesn't grow well with them.

Use the leaves, seeds and roots to soothe the stomach and relieve griping and wind as well as for its aromatic qualities. Use as an eye wash or gargle where inflammation is present.

In the kitchen
The seeds or leaves of fennel are used in moderate amounts in meat, fish, vegetable and egg dishes or in salads and vegetable juices.

Elder

Fennel

Feverfew

Pyrethrum parthenium
Family: Asteraceae (Compositae)
Also known as featherfew, featherfoil
or flirtwort.

The name 'feverfew' seems to have been derived from the word 'febrifuge', which describes the herb's properties of reducing fever. According to some old herbals, feverfew heals best if gathered with the left hand while speaking the name of the sick person, but under no circumstances must you look behind you while performing this ritual.

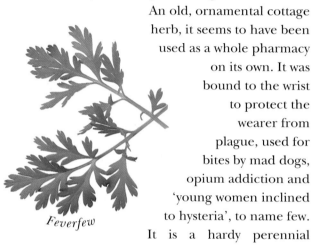

Feverfew

An old, ornamental cottage herb, it seems to have been used as a whole pharmacy on its own. It was bound to the wrist to protect the wearer from plague, used for bites by mad dogs, opium addiction and 'young women inclined to hysteria', to name few.

It is a hardy perennial growing 60–80cm (24–32in) tall, with alternate, light golden green leaves on a leafy, many-branched stem. The flowers are daisy-like with yellow centres and white rays with toothed edges. The plant self-seeds very easily and is an attractive addition to any garden.

The attractive flowers of feverfew can be used in floral arrangements which will last well indoors. Remember to replace the water every two days or so.

Grow it from seed in the sun with moderate water. It will resist frost and repel insects, but take

Caution:
Excessive use can cause vomiting and diarrhoea and, in rare cases, chewing the leaf can cause mouth ulcers, so take care to use it strictly according to directions.

care as it can invade the garden if not controlled.

Use the whole herb for its healing, sedative and tonic qualities and to soothe griping and wind. It can also be used to bring on a period. Use for relief of migraine headaches, arthritic inflammation and tinnitus.

Garlic

Allium sativum
Family: Liliaceae
Also known as poorman's treacle or
clove garlic.

Some say that a clove worn on a string around the neck will protect you from harm, especially by vampires. My theory is that you would smell so bad nobody would want to get close enough to damage you! However, garlic is one of the most trusted herbs and the smell should not stop you

A bunch of dried garlic amongst other dried herbs

using it. The myth probably came into being because of the great number of ailments which can be cured or alleviated by the use of garlic. Used on a daily basis it becomes a first-rate prophylactic.

A hardy perennial, it grows to about 30cm (1ft) high, with long, green, straplike leaves growing from leaf sheaths up the unbranched stem. On top of the stem, a clump of small, white florets are held together by a leaf-shaped skin. The bulb, at the base of the plant, is the most important part of the plant, both for cooking and medicinally. It is made up of a number of cloves or bulblets enclosed in a paper-like skin.

Grow it from root division in a sunny spot with moderate water. It will resist frost and provides a general insect repellent in the garden. Plant it near apple or peach trees, lettuce, parsnips or roses but away from beans, cabbage or strawberries.

Garlic

Use the bulb for its antiseptic, expectorant and cleansing properties, especially in treating earache, abcesses and ringworm. Use for all internal and external infections, high blood pressure and cholesterol.

In the kitchen

Garlic is a popular and mineral-rich food enhancer which contains vitamins A, B1, C and E, calcium, fluorine, iron, phosphorus, potassium, sulphur and zinc. Use it moderately in most savoury dishes with meat, fish or vegetables, soups, stews, salads, dressings and vinegars.

Caution:
Children need to be introduced very slowly to garlic. It's much better to use it in their food than to give pure garlic oil, which may cause problems in the young.

Ginger

Zingiber officinalis
Family: Zingiberaceae
Also known as African or race ginger.

Ginger has been a favourite for many centuries as a culinary and medicinal herb. It was mentioned by Confucius, 500 years before Christ, and is still used widely today in both Chinese and Western herbal medicine. It was one of the expensive and valuable trading spices. You will find a recipe for preserving ginger in Treats and Tempters.

Ginger is a perennial plant with a thick, fibrous, knotted root which is highly aromatic. The simple, reedlike stem grows to about 1m (3¼ft) high. The long, narrow leaves grow from sheaths on the stem. The yellowish-white flowers grow on spikes coming straight from the root.

Grow it from root division only if you are living in the tropics or sub-tropics or if you have a heated greenhouse or conservatory. It likes a sunny place and moderate water.

Ginger

The root (the part used) needs to be 12 months old before use. It has a stimulant, cleansing and expectorant action, helps to settle nausea and griping, promotes perspiration and has aromatic qualities. It is also used for boils, sprains and infected hangnails and alleviates pain. It improves circulation and helps to prevent or alleviate travel sickness and nausea.

In the kitchen

Ginger can be used moderately with beef, chicken, seafoods and vegetables, especially in spicy dishes like curries, as well as with cooked or fresh fruit dishes. It is also good in baking and in drinks, and small amounts can be tossed through salads or used in drinks and liqueurs.

Horseradish

Horseradish

Armoracia rusticana
Family: Brassicaceae (Cruciferae)
Also known as spoonwort, red cole or
mountain radish.

While living on the farm we grew lots of horseradish. One day we lifted a huge amount of the roots and began to process them, but the incredibly pungent fumes made our eyes stream, so we hit upon the idea of wearing diving masks. Of course, we were caught by visitors, adding further to our reputation for eccentricity. You will find a recipe for Horseradish Sauce on page 236.

This is a hardy perennial, very robust with a large, fleshy, pungent root. The lower leaves are yellowish-green, very large, shiny and pointed with wavy edges. As the leaves grow up the stem they become much smaller. In its second year a 60–90cm (2–3ft) stem grows from the root. On this, white, scented flowers are borne.

Grow it from root division but beware – the root is very invasive and will take over the garden if allowed. It grows best in the sun but is dormant in winter, likes moderate water and is resistant to frost. Plant it near apple or apricot trees or potatoes.

Use the root strictly according to directions as a diuretic and to stimulate the stomach secretions but take care. It improves circulation, and is used as an antiseptic for lungs and the urinary system. Horseradish can act as an emetic (induces vomiting) if used in large amounts.

Caution:
Horseradish should be avoided by those with depressed thyroid function.

In the kitchen
Horseradish goes well with beef, egg and vegetable dishes, sauces, salads, sandwiches, vegetable juices and dressings. Usually the root is used but the leaves go well in cold dishes.

Hyssop

Hyssopus officinalis
Family: Lamiaceae (Labiatae)

The name is derived from the Greek *azob* or *ezob*, meaning a holy herb, as it was used as an infusion for cleansing rites in holy places. There seems to be considerable confusion regarding the hyssop mentioned in the Bible. Some scholars maintain that the herb was not '*Hyssopus*' but either caper or oregano.

A perennial which can grow to 90cm (3ft) under the right conditions, the whole plant is bushy, with square, woody stems and opposite, long, narrow, dark green leaves, which have a sweet scent when bruised. The flowers are pink, blue or white, growing in whorls in the leaf bases.

Grow it from seed, cuttings, root division, mounding or layering in a sunny place with little water. It is frost-hardy and good to grow near cabbage or grapes but away from radishes. It is a general insect repellent and works well in sprays.

The whole herb is used for its stimulant, expectorant and perspiration-promoting qualities. It also helps abscesses, bruises (including black eyes), inflammation, rheumatism and sore throats. Particularly useful for children.

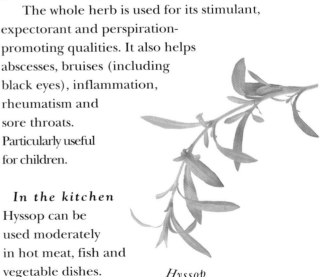

In the kitchen
Hyssop can be used moderately in hot meat, fish and vegetable dishes.

Hyssop

Lavender

Lavandula officinalis
Family: Lamiaceae (Labiatae)

Lavender

There is an old belief that if you want to remain chaste and virginal you must dry lavender flowers and sprinkle them upon your head. There are nearly 30 known species of lavender.

Most commonly cultivated for its precious oil is vera, known as angustifolia. This is a 60–90cm (2–3ft) plant with many straight, four-sided stems. The opposite, narrow, pointed leaves are greyish-green and covered with soft, downy hairs. Tiny mauve flowers are borne in clusters or whorls at the top of long spikes.

Lavender can also be used to make a wonderful perfumed soap

Other varieties include *Lavendula dentata*, which grows into quite a large shrub and is useful for hedging, provided it's pruned each year after flowering, to prevent it from becoming bare and woody at the base.

Lavendula allardi or *mitcham*, not always easy to obtain, has the benefits of the other lavenders in one plant. It can grow up to about 1.5m (5ft), with long flower heads on tall spikes and leaves like a cross between the French and English lavenders. The scent of lavender alone would make it worth growing and using in the home.

Grow it from cuttings or mounding and layering in a sunny place with little water. It is frost-resistant and a good companion to silver-beet. It repels beetles, mosquitoes, sandflies and flies and is a good indoor repellent.

Use the flowers, leaves and, most particularly, the essential oil for wound-healing, to calm nerves and spasms and to stimulate bile production and blood circulation.

In the kitchen

The flowers can be used to flavour sugar and jams. Crystallised lavender flowers make an attractive decoration on desserts.

Lemon Balm

Melissa officinalis
Family: Lamiaceae (Labiatae)
Also known as balm, honeyplant
or bee balm.

The name 'melissa' is derived from the Greek name for bee. Many records, both ancient and modern, suggest planting lemon balm near beehives and even rubbing the inside of the hive with leaves to keep the bees happy. To quote Gerard's *Herball* (1597):

> *'It is profitably planted where bees are kept.*
> *The hives of bees being rubbed with the leaves of bawme,*
> *causeth the bees to keep together,*
> *and causeth others to come with them.'*

It is a medium-sized perennial growing 60–90cm (2–3ft) tall, with a branched, square and somewhat hairy stem and opposite, light green, serrated leaves. Small, white flowers grow from the base of the leaves in small bunches.

Grow it from seed, cuttings, root division, mounding or layering in a semi-shaded place or indoors with moderate water. It will tolerate frost and can be used in general insect sprays.

The whole herb is used for its sedative, antispasmodic and stomach-settling qualities and its ability to promote perspiration and menstrual flow.

This is another herb suitable for children as it is mild, gentle and delicious.

In the kitchen

Lemon balm leaves add a sparkle to chicken and fish dishes, lamb, salads and desserts such as fruits and jellies. Use them in garnishes, drinks and dressings, too, for an extra tang.

Lemon Balm

Many records, both ancient and modern, suggest planting lemon balm near beehives and even rubbing the inside of the hive with leaves to keep the bees happy.

Lemon Grass

Lemon Grass

Cymbopogon citratus
Family: Poaceae (Graminacae)

Originating in Asia, the stems and base of the leaves of this plant are used to season Thai and Vietnamese dishes, especially curries, and peanut and saté sauces. It is a good herb for children, for refreshing drinks and for ornamental value in the garden. It grows well near a garden pond, where it looks very much at home with its tall, reed-like leaves reflected in the water.

A semi-hardy perennial, it grows in clumps to about 1m (3¼ft) in height. The leaves grow from the base, are pale green and reed-like. Grow it from root division in a sunny spot with lots of water. This plant doesn't like its feet to be either cold or dry and will not tolerate frosts. It dies back in winter and may be slow to recover in spring. In a warm climate, it grows a flowering stem but is unlikely to flower in cooler areas. Use the leaves for their cooling properties or just as a culinary herb.

In the kitchen

Use chopped lemon grass stems generously with chicken, curries and oriental cooking for a light, lemony flavour. Makes a refreshing tea.

Liquorice

Glycyrrhiza glabra
Family: Fabaceae (Leguminosae)
Also known as licorice root
or sweet licorice.

Many people prefer to buy the root from the health food store, as it takes four years for the plant to be ready to harvest. Even then, it has to be dried and ground into a powder or chopped. The other form in which it is used, as an extract available from pharmacies, cannot be made up at home at all.

Liquorice is an invaluable herb and one for which it's not easy to find an alternative. As well as its healing properties, it makes quite putrid-tasting herbs more acceptable to the palate, in tinctures, infusions and decoctions. This is of particular importance when treating children as they are very resistant to unfamiliar tastes but accept liquorice readily.

It is still worth growing this plant as it is large and handsome in the garden while you are waiting for it to mature. It is a perennial, initially slow-growing then spreading rapidly outward and up to 2m (6½ft) tall. The roots, which are the important part of this plant, are made up of two parts. One is long, brown, cylindrical and many-branched, while the other comprises horizontal rhizomes, which run just below the ground and throw up shoots, causing the plant to spread over a large area. Both parts of the root are used. From the roots rise many stems which are round at the base, becoming more angular further up. Small, dark green, graceful leaves stand up by day and droop at night. Mauve, pale blue or yellowish flowers grow from the axils.

Grow it from seed, root division or suckers but be careful to control it as it is invasive. It likes moderate water and a sunny position and will resist frosts.

The root is used for its anti-inflammatory, cleansing, softening and lubricating, expectorant and laxative qualities.

In the kitchen

Liquorice makes a delicious tea which can be served warm or cold.

> **Caution:**
> Regular or large doses of liquorice may be harmful for people with cardiovascular or kidney problems or diabetes.

Liquorice

Mallow

Mallow

Althaea species
Family: Malvaceae
Also known as common mallow, musk
mallow or dwarf mallow.

Marshmallow sweets were once made from the sticky extract of the mallow root and must have been very beneficial. Pliny said: 'Whosoever shall take a spoonful of the Mallows shall that day be free from all diseases that may come to him'. Now, however, they are far from being healthy as they are composed of sugar, gelatine, artificial colour and flavour.

The common mallow is the one used most often because of its availability. It can be seen almost everywhere, including roadsides and rubbish dumps. It is a biennial or perennial of quite straggly habit. It is branching with coarse, rounded, notched, slightly lobed leaves. The flowers are pink to mauve with dark purple vein markings on each heart-shaped petal. The root, the most important part of the plant, is thick, fleshy and greyish-white on the outside.

Grow it from seed in a sunny place with little water. It is frost-resistant.

Use the root, leaves and flowers in treating wounds and for its softening and cleansing qualities. It is particularly useful for burns, bruises, sprains, swellings and other inflammations, to ease stings and bites, soothe pain and heal ulcers. It soothes stomach and intestinal inflammation, and will help to loosen dry coughs.

In the kitchen

The flowers make a bright addition to salads along with the leaves and seeds. Even the mallow root can be added to casseroles and stews.

Marjoram

Origanum marjorana
Family: Lamiaceae (Labiatae)
Also known as sweet marjoram, knotted
marjoram or joy of the mountains.

The perfume in this herb is so intense that it was a favourite for 'strewing' in medieval days. One trembles to think what their houses must have smelt like to need such strong-smelling herbs underfoot! This powerful scent has a modern-day application as a 'smelling salt' to restore the faint or dizzy. Just holding a few crushed sprigs under the nose can restore them. Marjoram and oregano have similar properties, including their antiseptic power, which can act in a prophylactic manner if used frequently in cooking – a good example of preventive medicine.

It is a perennial but is best treated as an annual as it tends to become straggly and woody in its second year. It grows to about 30cm (1ft), with a many-branched, square stem, bearing opposite, greyish-green, small, rounded leaves and flowers like clusters of little knots.

Grow it from seed, cuttings, mounding or layering in a sunny, frost-free place or indoors. It will repel ants and bacteria and is a good companion to cucumber.

The whole herb is used for its tonic powers and to stimulate menstrual flow. It is also used to treat fainting, abscesses, bruises, earache, inflammation and pain, and to heal cuts and wounds, sprains and swellings.

Marjoram

In the kitchen

Marjoram leaves add flavour to cooked meat, vegetable, seafood and vegetable dishes. It is best added late in the cooking.

Mint

Spearmint – Mentha viridis
Peppermint – Mentha piperita
Family: Lamiaceae (Labiatae)
Also known as garden mint, Our Lady's
mint, lamb mint, brandy mint.

There are, of course, many more varieties of mint than we can list here but these two are the most useful herbal mints. With all varieties (especially if you grow more than one) it is essential to pick off all flower heads as they bloom or they will cross-pollinate each other and the plant will become a coarse-leaved and not so useful 'bastard' mint, lacking any distinct flavour or perfume of peppermint or spearmint.

Mint is a perennial with a creeping rootstock, growing mostly to about 30cm (1ft) tall. Spearmint stems are square with bright green, short-stemmed, pointed leaves with irregularly serrated edges and pale lilac flowers in whorls at the top of the stem. Peppermint is similar but with darker green leaves, purple-tinged stems and darker flowers. The whole plant has a distinctive menthol odour.

Grow mints from seed or runners in semi-shade or indoors with lots of water. They tolerate frost and repel mice, caterpillars, and cabbage moth, the latter making them good companions for cabbages. Take care, as they are invasive and can take over the garden.

Use the leaves and stems of both varieties for their antispasmodic and aromatic qualities and to soothe indigestion, wind and griping problems. Spearmint will also soothe pain, relieve nausea and promote perspiration, cooling the body, as well as providing a general tonic. Peppermint aids digestion and acts as a stimulant and a diuretic.

Use spearmint for children in preference to peppermint as the action in gentler.

In the kitchen

Mints are extremely useful in cooking. The leaves go well with fish, lamb, vegetables and stewed fruit dishes, especially when added late in the cooking. Use them in salads and fruit salads, drinks, dressings, vinegars and as garnishes, fresh or crystallised.

Peppermint

Spearmint

A herb garden with borage and eau de cologne mint which can be used in colognes and potpourri

Mullein

Verbascum thapsus
Family: Scrophulariaceae
Also known as great mullein, lady's
foxglove, blanket herb, flannel plant, and
many more.

In medieval days, the tall flower stalk of the mullein would be dried, dipped in melted tallow and lit, to carry through the streets as a torch lighting the way for processions.

Mullein is a tall, handsome biennial growing up to 2m (6½ft) in good conditions, with huge, woolly, grey-green base leaves, which become smaller and alternate up the stem of the plant. The tall, straight stem grows in the second year and may be simple or branched. The flowers are bright yellow and heavily clustered on the top 30cm (1ft) of the stem.

Grow it from seed in a sunny position with moderate water. It is frost-resistant.

Use the leaves and flowers to ease pain and spasms and for its cleansing and expectorant properties. It is used to treat arthritis, bronchitis, bursitis, cysts, swollen glands, inflammation, neuralgia, sore nipples and sore throats. If you can find wild mullein in a clean, unpolluted area (the wild version is shorter with much smaller, dark green leaves), its medicinal properties are

reputed to be more powerful than the cultivated variety. But be sure of your identification before using this or any wild herb!

In the kitchen

Mullein flowers can be used to flavour liqueurs.

Nasturtium

Tropaeolum majus or minus
Family: Brassicaceae (Cruciferae)
Also known as Indian cress.

Nasturtium belongs to the same family as watercress and has the same peppery 'bite'. After treatment, the seeds may be pickled and used like capers (see Condiments). Nasturtium has an anti-infective action and for this reason is included in our food as often as possible.

An annual, self-seeding, creeping and climbing plant, its leaves are round, flat, smooth and pale green, with bright, showy trumpet-shaped flowers, ranging from pale yellow through to dark red.

Nasturtium

Grow it from seed in a sunny, frost-free place with moderate water. It repels beetles and aphis and is good to plant near apple trees, broccoli, Brussels sprouts, cabbage, cauliflower, cucumber, grapes, kohlrabi, radishes and zucchini. It is a lovely and useful herb to grow in your garden but can become a pest by growing so rampantly that it suffocates and chokes any plants in its path.

A mullein plant

Overcome this problem by pinching off the tips of all shoots when they are a suitable length for you, or buy seeds of the new 'non-running' varieties.

Use the leaves, flowers and seeds for their antiseptic and expectorant qualities.

In the kitchen

Nasturtium leaves can be used in cheese and egg dishes. Try the flowers in soups and stewed fruit. Leaves or flowers can be added to cottage cheese, salads, sandwiches and used as garnishes.

Nasturtium flowers and leaves are delicious in salads and the seeds can be pickled

Nettle

Urtica dioica
Family: Urticaceae

To most people this is a despised weed, yet it deserves a place of honour in your garden, perhaps in a corner where it can quietly grow and multiply without stinging anyone. It is a most wonderful herb, full of vitamins and minerals. It makes a delicious soup and a first-rate treatment for hair and its uses extend even to the making of a cloth very similar to linen.

In Scotland I have eaten nettles,
slept in nettle sheets and dined off a nettle
tablecloth.
My mother thought nettle cloth more durable
than any species of linen.

— CAMBELL

There are two types of nettle. One is an annual with a delicate pale green, opposite leaf and shallow root system, rarely growing more than 25–30cm (10–12in) tall. The other is a perennial with a much coarser, darker leaf and a creeping rootstock. The leaves of both are hairy, deeply serrated, and pointed. The whole plant is covered with sharp stinging points which cause intense irritation and local swelling. In Britain, where dock grows near nettle patches, a crushed dock leaf rubbed onto the sting gives instant relief. Elsewhere, other local herbs might have to be tried!

Nettle

It can be grown from seed, with little water in a sunny spot but it will tend to invade the garden and it must always be handled with gloves. Collect it from the wild if possible, as this not only saves your garden but wild herbs tend to be more potent. Use it in a general spray for the health of the garden.

The whole herb is used (suitably processed!) to stop bleeding, cleanse and heal wounds and for its diuretic, astringent, nutritional and tonic qualities.

In the kitchen

Nettle is difficult to handle because of its sting. This herb is mineral-rich to eat and loses the sting when cooked. Only use the leaves of *young* nettles in vegetable dishes and stews. (Use gloves to handle it when raw!)

Nettle in, dock out.
Dock rub, nettle out!
AN OLD RHYME

Oregano

Origanum vulgare
Family: Lamiaceae (Labiatae)
Also known as wild marjoram or
mountain mint.

Argument continues among botanists and herbalists about the identity of the 'true' oregano. There are so many varieties that my tip would be to find the one with the strongest flavour and perfume and stick to that. Oregano and marjoram are among the few herbs that retain their pungent and distinctive aroma after drying. The flowers also carry the perfume, to an even greater extent than the leaves. This is rare in the herb world and means that the plant can be collected while in full flower and both flowers and leaves dried for use.

A perennial plant with a creeping rootstock, it has purple-tinged woody stems, usually up to 60–70cm (24–28in), with opposite, small, bright to dark green rough-textured leaves. The white or pale purple flowers grow in terminal clusters.

Oregano

Grow it from seed or root division in the sun or indoors. It is frost-resistant and likes moderate water. It repels bacteria and ants and is good near cabbage or cucumber.

Use the whole herb for its antispasmodic, expectorant and tonic qualities and its ability to soothe stomach disorders and griping and to promote perspiration.

In the kitchen

Oregano leaves add flavour to cooked meat, fish, vegetable and egg dishes, soups and stews. Add towards the end of cooking. Use more sparingly to enhance dressed salads, vegetable dishes and vinegars.

Parsley

Common Parsley

Continental Parsley

Petroselinum crispum
Family: Apiaceae (Umbelliferae)
Also known as persely, persele, common parsley.

There are many myths surrounding parsley – that it will only grow in gardens where the woman is 'master' of the household, that the seed has to go to the devil and back seven times before it will germinate – and many more.

There can be few people who don't recognise and use this herb, though there are many who don't recognise its potential. It is commonly used as a garnish for food but it is rare for anyone to eat the garnish. This is a pity, as the parsley sprig ensures well-digested food, sweet breath and a good supply of minerals and vitamins.

Of the many types of parsley available, the crispum is the most widely used. It is a biennial with bright green foliage, deeply divided, curling leaves and a flower stem in the second year with tiny white/green flowers. Grow it from seed in a frost-free, sunny place or indoors with moderate water. To prolong the life of the plant, cut the stem right back or the plant will go to seed and die. Plant it near asparagus, roses or tomatoes.

The root, leaves and seeds are used for their digestive and diuretic qualities.

In the kitchen

Vitamin-rich parsley leaves can be added to almost any savoury dish, hot or cold, including dressings and vegetable juices. It makes an excellent garnish.

Caution:
Do not use parsley remedies or medications if your kidneys are inflamed and always use the correct dose as excessive quantities can damage the liver and kidneys.

The parsley sprig ensures well-digested food, sweet breath and a good supply of vitamins and minerals

Pennyroyal

Mentha pulegium
Family: Lamiaceae (Labiatae)
Also known as European pennyroyal or lurk-in-the-ditch.

Pennyroyal has a reputation for driving fleas away. Pliny called this herb *pulegium* (*pulex* is the Latin word for flea). The name, lurk-in-the-ditch, is very apt. I know a watery ditch down a little-used lane which is rampant with pennyroyal in the spring. I collect armfuls and drive home with the car windows open; otherwise the powerful scent gives me a headache.

Pennyroyal

A perennial herb with a creeping rootstock, it grows 20–30cm (8–12in) tall, with weak, prostrate stems. It roots very readily where nodes touch the ground. The leaves are opposite, small and bright green, quite unlike others of the mint family, and the pale purple flowers grow in clusters.

Grow it from seed or root division in the shade or indoors with lots of water. In the garden, it makes a good ground cover and is frost-resistant. Rub the dried, powdered herb into your pet's coat.

Use the whole herb for its sedative and perspiration-promoting qualities and to relieve griping and stimulate menstrual flow.

In the kitchen

A sprinkling of chopped leaves can be added to soups and salads.

Caution:
Pennyroyal should not be used during pregnancy.

Plantain

Plantain

Plantago major and Plantago lanceolata
Family: Plantaginaceae
Also known as common plantain, broad-leaved plantain, lanceleaf plantain, ribwort or white man's foot.

One of the 'nine sacred herbs', (see chamomile) plantain grows everywhere in the world where the white man has been, thus the name, white man's foot. Like the nettle, it is treated as a pest by those who don't know its worth. Make a place for it in your garden and learn to appreciate its virtues.

Plantago major is a perennial 'weed', with a radial rosette of wide, ribbed, greyish-green, hairy leaves which can grow 25–30cm (10–12in) long. The flower stalk is erect, 30–40cm (12–16in) tall, with greyish-green, inconspicuous flowers on the top, almost covered by brown bracts.

Plantago lanceolata has bright green, pointed and ribbed leaves and a grooved flower stalk from 20–60cm (8–24in) high, topped with a flower head 1–2cm (about $\frac{1}{2}$in) long, with slim, white filaments tipped with greenish-yellow anthers forming a halo round the base of the head.

Grow it from seed in a sunny position with moderate water or, if you do not want it invading your garden, find it in the wild.

Use the leaves and seeds for their astringent and cleansing qualities to heal wounds, boils, ringworm, sores, stings and bites and to reduce black eyes and swellings, haemorrhoids, swollen glands, varicose veins, cysts and cystitis. Use to help ease a dry cough.

Raspberry

Rubus idaeus
Family: Rosaceae
Also known as red raspberry, hindberry
or wild raspberry.

I often took my dachshunds walking in the woods in Dorset. The dogs would race ahead chasing real or imagined rabbits, but in late summer and early autumn the hunt became serious. I would hear high-pitched barking and know they had found raspberry bushes. They were far too shrewd (and also too short) to pick the berries – this chore was left to me – but they would eat the berries for as long as I was prepared to pick them. This led me to the discovery that dogs love fruit if it's offered to them from an early age.

A well-known plant with perennial roots and prickly, biennial stems, growing to about 1–2m ($3\frac{1}{4}$–$6\frac{1}{2}$ft). The leaves are feather-shaped with 3–7 notched lobes, green above, whitish-green and hairy beneath. The loose, small, greenish-white flowers turn to red, compound fruits, ripening during the summer. They are strongly scented and delicious.

Grow them from cuttings in the sun with moderate water. They are frost-resistant but invasive so need to be controlled in your garden.

Use the leaves and fruit as an astringent gargle for mouth and throat infections and other infections. Take for the last 3 months of pregnancy to ease and improve labour.

In the kitchen
The fruit can be eaten plain or in fruit salads, or puréed into sauces.

Raspberry

Red Clover

Trifolium pratense
Family: Fabaceae (Leguminosae)
Also known as purple clover or
trefoil.

This is a well-known fodder and soil improvement plant, a nitrogen fixer used by farmers in many countries. Very valuable to the herbalist, it has wide applications but needs lots of space to grow any reasonable quantity, so is often best sprouted in the same way as alfalfa (see Sprouting).

Red Clover

Red clover is a perennial with 30–60cm (1–2ft) stalks rising from a short rootstock. Bright green, three-lobed leaves are sometimes finely toothed on the leaflets. The flowers grow in dense globular heads and vary considerably in colour from deep red to white.

Grow it from seed in a sunny place with moderate water or sprout it in the kitchen.

Use the flowers or sprouted whole herb for its powerful cleansing, diuretic and expectorant qualities. Particularly useful in the treatment of skin diseases.

In the kitchen
Red clover sprouts are vitamin-rich. Add them late in cooking to cheese, egg, rice and vegetable dishes and in soups and stews. They are also good in leafy salads, sandwiches, cottage cheese and as a garnish.

Rosemary

Rosmarinus officinalis
Family: Lamiaceae (Labiatae)
Also known as compass plant, romero,
polar plant or herb of remembrance.

Rosemary is known as the 'herb of remembrance' and is dedicated to lovers. However, this herb is used medicinally to improve brainpower and failing memory, so perhaps this is the origin of the name – not so romantic but maybe more accurate. It was always included in bridal bouquets as the herb of love and loyalty and used on many occasions when solemn vows of honour and fidelity were being sworn. In Wales it was the custom to carry a sprig of rosemary to a funeral and throw it on the coffin as it was being lowered into the grave.

Rosemary

One of the best known and loved herbs, rosemary is a perennial shrub growing up to 2m (6½ft) under good conditions. It is many-branched with opposite, narrow, shiny, leathery leaves which are a rich dark green on top and pale underneath.

The flowers are small, pale to dark blue. The whole plant is very aromatic if bruised and the leaves exude a sticky resin when stripped from the branches.

Grow it from cuttings, mounding or layering in the sun with little water. It resists frost and repels beetles, cabbage moth, carrot fly and fleas. Plant it with cabbage or carrots but away from potatoes or tomatoes.

Use the leaves and flowers to heal wounds, cuts, sores, stings and bites. They relieve spasms, induce perspiration and the flow of bile, calm the nerves and provide a tonic, and restorative to the nervous system. Stimulates the circulation.

Caution:
Do not take rosemary in large doses or over extended periods of time and never take the oil internally.

In the kitchen

Rosemary is especially good with chicken, lamb, vegetable, eggs and in sauces and stews. The leaves can also be added to biscuits, salads and fruit salads, liqueurs, pickles, vegetable juices, vinegars, punches and as a garnish.

Rue

Ruta graveolens
Family: Rutaceae
Also known as herb of grace, herby grass,
herb of repentance.

Rue has been in use for more than 2000 years. It seems to have been one of the main herbs used against plague and witchcraft. Judges in court were, until quite recently, given 'tussie mussies' (small bouquets) or sprigs of rue. It was believed that the perfume would protect them from the jail fever being carried by the prisoners. Rue was one of the ingredients in the 'vinegar of the four thieves', used by a band of robbers employed by a French pharmacist to rob the bodies and homes of the dead during the plague. The vinegar was used as a wash to prevent the thieves from catching the disease. We never learnt how effective it was, but herbal vinegar makes a good air spray, wound wash and bath additive.

Rue is a shrubby little perennial with a smooth, pale green, branched stem, alternate, smallish leaves of an unusual metallic blue-green, yellow flowers and a pungent smell. The plant rarely grows more than 60–80cm (24–32in).

Grow it from seed or cuttings in a sunny place with little water. It repels ants, fleas, flies, snails and slugs. Plant it away from cabbages.

Use the leaves to relieve spasms, upset stomachs and griping, to promote menstrual flow and as a circulatory and uterine stimulant.

Rue

He who would live for aye, must eat sage in May.
OLD ENGLISH PROVERB

Tis a plant indeed with so many and wonderful properties as that the assiduous use of it said to render men immortal.
JOHN EVELYN

Sage

Salvia officinalis
Family: Lamiaceae (Labiatae)
Also known as garden sage or sawge.

Sage is a hardy perennial of shrubby habit, growing to about 30cm (1ft), with opposite, slightly hairy, greyish-green, oblong leaves and purple flowers.

Grow it from seed or cuttings in a sunny spot with little water. It is frost resistant and repels cabbage moth, carrot fly, snails and slugs. Grow it near cabbage, carrots or strawberries.

Use the leaves for their anti-inflammatory and astringent qualities to treat abscesses, sores, ulcers, wounds and varicose veins. It is also good for the liver and promotes the production of bile. Keep a very strong sage infusion in the freezer for rapid relief from any mouth or throat problems. Sucking sage ice cubes helps heal mouth ulcers. Reduces excessive perspiration and 'night sweats'.

Sage

In the kitchen
Sage is particularly good in savoury dishes and can be used with vegetables, poultry, soups, stews, stuffings, cottage cheese and dressings.

Savory

Summer savory, also known as bean herb:
Satureia hortensis
Winter savory: Satureia montana
Family: Lamiaceae (Labiatae)

Keep it dry, make conserves and syrups of it
for your use;
for which purpose the summer kind is best.
This kind is both hotter and drier than the
winter kind.
It expels tough phlegm from the chest and
lungs,
and quickens the dull spirits in lethargy.
– ANON

Summer savory is a bushy annual which grows to about 60cm (2ft) high with opposite, long straight leaves and pinkish-mauve flowers in clusters. Winter savory is much smaller, perennial, branched and woody with dark green glossy leaves and lots of creamy white flowers from midsummer until the end of autumn.

Grow savory from seed or the winter variety also from cuttings, mounding or layering, in a sunny spot with moderate water. Summer savory is frost tender (it will grow indoors) but winter savory is frost-resistant. Savory repels beetles and grows well with beans.

Use the leaves as an astringent, stimulant or expectorant, or to soothe the stomach or griping pains.

Savory

In the kitchen
Savory (summer and winter) is good to flavour delicate dishes such as cheese, egg, poultry and vegetable dishes. It is also good in salads, cottage cheese or dressings. Winter savory is particularly good with beans as it reduces the 'flatulence factor'.

Shepherd's Purse

Capsella bursa-pastoris
Family: Brassicaceae (Cruciferae)
Also known as shepherd's bag, lady's
purse, pickpocket or toywort.

Another invaluable herb which is often viewed as a weed. Give shepherd's purse a special place in a 'wild' area of your garden.

An annual, it can vary 15–30cm (6–12in) in height depending on the growing conditions. The main leaves, which are green, rough, and divided like a feather, form a rosette from which the erect stem rises to tiny, white flowers. The small, flat, heart-shaped pods (like old-fashioned purses) are the best way to identify this plant.

Grow it from seed in a sunny place with moderate water or gather it from the wild if you do not want it to invade your garden.

Use the whole plant for its stimulant, antiseptic, wound-healing properties and to stop bleeding. It can be used to help to control internal haemorrhage and might even save your life in an emergency.

Shepherd's Purse

Southernwood

Artemisia abrotanum
Family: Asteraceae (Compositae)
Also known as old man, lad's love,
garderobe.

This plant was reputed to promote hair growth. Used as an ointment and rubbed on the chin, it was said to grow beards on young men, making

Southernwood

them more attractive to the girls. Small bouquets would be taken to church and sniffed to ward off sleepiness during lengthy sermons. The sharp scent would certainly achieve this.

It is a small, perennial shrub, rarely exceeding 90cm (3ft) in height. It has grey-green finely divided leaves and a very strong, aromatic, lemony smell, which makes it a fine insect repellent. The pale yellow flowers bloom in summer in small, loose, inconspicuous bunches.

Grow it from cuttings in the sun with little water. It resists frost and is a good companion to apricot trees, giving general insect-repellent protection.

Use the leaves to stimulate the appetite, improve digestion, and as a general stimulant and tonic. It also increases menstrual flow.

In the kitchen

The leaves can be used in cakes such as the Southernwood Cake in Desserts (Chapter six).

Caution:
Avoid during pregnancy.

Tansy

Tanacetum vulgare
Family: Asteraceae (Compositae)
Also known as buttons, bachelor's buttons or stinking willie.

One of the most interesting uses of tansy in the past was as an embalming agent and a meat preservative. It is a useful herb for those with pets as it helps keep the flea population under control. Tansy is a hardy perennial which spreads from runners. It is almost as invasive as the mint family. The rootstock sends up an erect, grooved, leafy stem which grows to a height of about 90cm (3ft), with alternate, fern-like dark green leaves and attractive flat, yellow clusters of button-like flowers developing in early autumn.

Grow it from root division in a sunny spot with moderate water. It resists frost and repels ants, aphis, beetles, cabbage moth, cutworm and acts as a general insecticide indoors. It is a good companion to apple, peach and apricot trees; cabbage; cauliflower; grapes; raspberries; and even roses.

Use the whole herb to treat inflammations, cuts, sprains and varicose veins.

Tansy

Caution:
Over-large doses of tansy can be fatal. Do not use internally except with professional advice and under supervision.

Tarragon

Artemisia dranunculus
Family: Asteraceae (Compositae)
*Also known as little dragon, estragon or
French tarragon.*

A semi-hardy perennial, tarragon grows to about 70cm (28in) in height. It is bushy but has a rather sprawly habit, with long, narrow, dark green, leaves and small, insignificant flowers. Don't let yourself be fobbed off with Russian tarragon – it is very inferior in flavour.

Grow it from root division in a sunny spot with moderate water. It is dormant in winter but resistant to frost. True French tarragon will rarely grow from seed. The inferior Russian tarragon grows readily from seed, but packets of seeds rarely mention the variety. So beware – it is much better to beg or buy a piece of root from an established plant.

Use the leaves as a diuretic, to stimulate menstrual flow and to soothe the stomach or just as a delightful culinary herb.

Tarragon

In the kitchen

Tarragon is best with delicate foods such as seafood, poultry, eggs, cheese and vegetables, it is also excellent in salads, dressings and vinegars and can be used as a garnish.

Thyme

Garden thyme or common thyme:
Thymus vulgaris
Lemon thyme: Thymus citriodorus
Family: Lamiaceae (Labiatae)

There are many varieties of thyme with slight differences in aroma and appearance and they are often used as ground covers in cottage gardens. Garden thyme is a small, bushy perennial with hard, branching stems growing about 25cm (10in) high. The leaves are very small, opposite, and greyish-green in colour. Light purple flowers are borne from late spring onwards. Lemon thyme is very similar but slightly smaller, with brighter green foliage and a slightly darker mauve flower. It's not as strong medicinally but is such a wonderful culinary herb that it is worth growing.

Lemon Thyme

Garden Thyme

Grow thymes from seed, root division, mounding or layering in the sun or indoors with moderate water. Some can grow indoors. They are frost-resistant and spreading in habit. They repel cabbage moth, black fly and some bacteria and are a good companion to Brussels sprouts, cabbage, broccoli and cauliflower.

Thyme growing amongst a herb garden

Use the leaves to treat arthritis, bronchitis, rheumatism, cuts, sores, wounds and ulcers. It works as an anti-inflammatory, an antispasmodic and an expectorant. It also aids digestion and acts as a tonic.

Caution:
Take no more than 1–4g dried leaf daily. Not to be taken for longer than 3 weeks at a time.

In the kitchen

The leaves of culinary thymes can be used to flavour most meat and vegetable dishes, seafood, eggs and cheese. It also makes excellent vinegars and can be used as a garnish.

Valerian

Valeriana officinalis
Family: Valerianaceae
Also known as setwall, all-heal, amantilla or fragrant valerian.

The flowers of this plant smell bad and the root, after drying, even worse. But this evil-smelling root, containing valerianic, formic and acetic acids, pinene and borneol plus isovalerianic acid (this gives the evil smell), provides us with one of nature's finest remedies for nerves and spasms. It is best used in compounds as it is easier to disguise the taste in this way. It is said that it was used by the Pied Piper of Hamelin to lure rats out of the city. The scent of the bruised root does seem to attract them.

It is a hardy perennial with one hollow, furrowed stem rising to a height of about 1m (3¼ft), usually in the second year of growth. The large leaves are pale green, opposite and serrated

Valerian

and the stem divides to form flower stems with clusters of small pink flowers at the top.

Grow it from root division in a sunny spot with moderate water. It resists frost but is dormant in winter.

Use the root at the end of the second year of growth for its pain and anxiety-relieving, calming and antispasmodic qualities. It also helps heal wounds, relieve cramps and muscular tension.

Violet

Viola odorata
Family: Violaceae
Also known as sweet violet or garden violet.

In both ancient and modern days, in East and West, the violet has always been a favourite flower. In France, during the days of troubadours, the prize awarded to the best poet was a beautiful golden violet.

This little perennial plant must surely be known by everyone, with its heart-shaped leaves and sweet-scented flowers ranging in colour from pink through to royal purple.

Violet

Propagation is by runners and unless the plant is regularly divided it will produce very few flowers. It likes a shady spot with moderate water and will resist frosts.

The whole plant can be used to heal sores and ulcers, to reduce inflammation, to promote perspiration and as an expectorant and diuretic.

In the kitchen

Violet flowers can be added to salads or can be crystallised and make beautiful decorations on cakes and desserts.

Watercress and Landcress

Watercress

Landcress

Nasturtium officinalis
Lapidium sativum
Family: Brassicaceae (Cruciferae)

Watercress is a perennial, creeping plant, which needs cool, fresh water to grow. The leaves are glossy, brownish-green, while the flowers are small and white. Landcress, also known as American up-land cress, is much easier to grow than watercress. An annual with dark green, shiny leaflets growing up a pale green, sappy, grooved stem, its flower stalk rises above the leaves and has small yellow blooms. The flavour is more pungent than that of watercress. This herb should not be eaten while flowering. If you don't want to save the seeds you can cut the flower stalks off to ensure a continuing supply of leaves for the table.

Grow landcress from seed in a sunny spot with moderate water or watercress from runners with plenty of water. It can invade the garden so you may prefer to find it in the wild or just sprout the seeds for the kitchen. Be very careful if you are collecting watercress in the wild as it can harbour liver fluke. Check with your local agriculture department to find out if this pest is in your neighbourhood.

Use the whole herb as a diuretic, stimulant, tonic and expectorant and to soothe the stomach. It is very valuable for its vitamin and mineral content.

In the kitchen

Cress makes a particularly good mineral-rich soup, excellent in salads and sandwiches.

While Wormwood hath seed, get
a handful of twaine,
To save against March, to make
flea to refrain:
When chamber is sweep'd, and
wormwood is strowne,
No flea, for his life, dare abide
to be known.
What savour is better, if Physic
be true,
For places infected than
wormwood or Rue?
It is a comfort for heart and the
brain,
And therefore to have it is not in
vain.

– Thomas Tusser: Five
Hundred
Pointes of Good
Husbandry, 1573

Wormwood

Artemisia absinthium
Family: Asteraceae (Compositae)
Also known as old woman, green ginger and absinthe.

A bushy perennial growing about 1m (3¼ft) high, with stems and leaves covered with fine, whitish hairs, giving the plant a silvery appearance. The alternate, long, divided leaves complement numerous, small, yellow, round flower heads.

Caution:
Excessive or prolonged use of this plant can cause poisoning. Use 1–4g dried herb or equivalent daily for no longer than 3 weeks.

Grow it from seed in a sunny place with moderate water. It is frost-resistant and repels beetles, cabbage moth, carrot fly, snails and slugs and makes a good general insecticide for indoors and out.

Use the leaves and flowering tops for their appetite-stimulant and stomach-soothing qualities and to treat cystitis, neuralgia, rheumatism and sprains.

Wormwood

Yarrow

Achillea millefolium
Family: Asteraceae (Compositae)
Also known as milfoil, thousand leaf or nosebleed.

Achilles is said to have used this plant to stem the bleeding wounds of his soldiers, hence the name Achillea. To this day the stiff, straight flower stalks are dried and used in the casting of the *I Ching*, an ancient Chinese oracle.

This is a perennial plant growing 30–40cm (12–16in) in height, with alternate, fine, feathery leaves and small, white, daisy-like flowers in flattened terminal heads. There is a variety of yarrow with much coarser, large leaves and scarlet heads, which can be used in the same way as milfoil variety.

Grow it from root division in a sunny spot with moderate water but beware, as it can take over the garden. It will resist frost and makes a good general insecticide.

Use the leaves and flowers to reduce bleeding and heal wounds, promote perspiration, aid digestion and for its stimulant

Yarrow

and tonic qualities. It is used to treat abscesses, sores, wounds and cuts, bruises, sore nipples, swollen glands and sore throats. The classic colds, flu and fever remedy among herbalists is an infusion made of yarrow, peppermint and elderflower.

Yellow Dock

Rumex crispus
Family: Polygonacae
Also known as curled dock, narrow dock or garden patience.

Yellow Dock is a perennial plant whose stem grows about 30–90cm (1–3ft). The root (which is the important part of the herb) grows very deep, 23–30cm (9–12in) long, and about 1cm (½in) thick. It has a rusty brown, quite thick bark with whitish flesh. It is very difficult to eradicate, hence its unpopularity with gardeners. The long, pointed, light green leaves have crisped or wavy edges and become progressively smaller up the stem. The pale green flowers are followed by brown seeds with three angles.

Although the plant can be grown from seed with little water in your garden, it is invasive and can take over. To prevent this, cut the flower heads off as they develop.

Use the root for its astringent and tonic qualities and its ability to stimulate the flow of bile. It is used to treat cystitis, swollen glands, sores, sore throats, sprains and swellings.

Yellow Dock

CHAPTER TWO

GROWING HERBS

Forget the garden which contains separate vegetable patches,

herb areas and flower beds. Grow instead a profusion of

vibrant colour and perfume where basil rubs cheeks with

tomatoes; calendulas with beans; fruit trees receive protection

from chives and nasturtiums; roses luxuriate and share with

garlic and parsley.

Let the herbs protect and nourish the whole garden, not

languish alone in a modest corner.

Give all the plants the space they need, plenty of rich, sweet

compost to feed the soil, enough water, and every excursion

you make into the garden will provide a feast of colour for the

eyes, perfume for the nose and music for the ears as bees,

birds and insects flock to enjoy its richness.

As I write these words I remember my home in North Wales when I was a teenager. Grey stone walls with windows overlooking heather-purple mountains, valleys and caves where foxes raised their cubs, and the north window framing the turbulent, exciting ocean between us and Ireland. In the kitchen there was a dark oak Welsh dresser, beeswaxed until it reflected the blue and white pots standing on it, and a floor of red quarry tiles washed with buttermilk which gave it a rich warm glow in the firelight. Hanging from the black oak beams were home-smoked hams, strings of black puddings and bunches of herbs gathered from the meadows, river edge and hillsides.

The larder off the kitchen was built into the hill, making it as cold as any refrigerator. It had a huge marble bench on which red salmon (caught in the river by my father), fresh milk and buttermilk stayed cold and delicious. It also housed home-churned butter wrapped in sorrel leaves, a bowl of fresh eggs and, if we were lucky, a clove and apple pie with a fragrance to make your mouth water. Hanging from the ceiling was a pheasant and a rabbit or two, tribute to my father's prowess with the gun and also to his delicacy – he never took from the sky, river or fields more than his family could eat or trade with friends. On the floor stood stone bottles of dandelion and burdock wine which I was allowed only in medicinal doses. How I longed for more.

I look back with nostalgia on these days of my youth which I took so much for granted – I remember complaining at the dinner table, 'Not pheasant again!'. We can't return to our childhood, but we can do as much as we are able to create a safe, wholesome and happy environment for our families.

It has been said that wild herbs are more potent than herbs grown in a garden and this may well be true, but these days they are also more contaminated. In this section you will find many ways to ensure that your plants are full of vigour and goodness. You will discover how to grow your herbs, how to harvest, dry and store them, and how to use them as companion plants and also insect repellents.

If you wish to begin with only a few plants, choose those repeated most often through the book. In this way, you will begin with a selection that has wide application. If you have very little space, find a selection of small herbs that will suit you. For instance, if you have a pocket-sized garden you will not be able to grow angelica, bay or elder. Perhaps you can find a few friends who also want to grow herbs and divide the cost and growing between you. You will benefit in lots of ways – shared interest, expense and space.

If you have never grown herbs before, you are about to experience a very joyful time as you watch the plants grow, gather them and turn them into the exciting things in this book. You will also see the benefits to your garden as the herbs give their minerals to the soil and their essential oils to the air.

Many people think that a garden is made up of a herb patch, some flower beds and the vegetable plot. In my garden, a border may be woolly yarrow, parsley or some other low-growing herb, and silverbeet grows cheek by jowl with roses and borage – a great colour combination. Tomatoes, capsicums and other vegetables share very happily with the herbs and flowers. The only precaution you need to take is to make sure the vegetables get the extra space and food that they always need.

From now on, be very careful of well-wishers who offer to do some weeding for you. It's more than likely you will find your precious dandelions, shepherd's purse and plantain in a dying pile and your friend very happy at having done such a good job. You will develop a whole new attitude towards 'weeds' when you realise they are all valuable, though not necessarily in the position they have chosen to grow. Give them their own place and watch them flourish.

GARDENING TERMS

This is a very short list of terms, sufficient for the scope of this book. If you want to know more, consult one of the many good books on organic gardening which are now available.

ACID	Soil, water etc, with a pH level below 7.0, indicating the absence of lime. A simple soil test can be done at home using litmus paper. Put a tablespoon of soil in a non-metal dish, cover with water, and when it has settled dip the paper into the water. If the paper is red then the soil is acid, if blue it is alkaline. If you'd like a more accurate test you can buy a testing kit. The application of good compost balances most soils; however, if you have azaleas or other acid-loving plants in your garden, you must remember to mulch them with pine needles, sawdust or other acidic materials.
ALKALINE	Soil, water etc, with a pH above 7.0. See ACID.
ANNUAL	Completing a whole life cycle in one year.
BIENNIAL	A plant which fruits in its second year and then dies.
DAMPING OFF	A condition in which a seedling rots at the base where it touches the soil. 'Damping off' is usually a fungal problem.
DRILL	A channel made in soil to sow seed, usually twice as deep as the circumference of the seed.
HUMUS	Decomposed organic matter.
LITMUS PAPER	See ACID.
MULCH	Material laid around plants to protect the roots, conserve moisture, or deter the growth of unwanted plants, e.g. straw, grass clippings, newspaper, rocks.
NODE	A sometimes swollen joint where a leaf joins a stem.
PERENNIAL	A plant which lives for more than two years.
SLAKED LIME	Otherwise known as hydrate of lime. This is quicklime which has been treated with water, making it less caustic and more readily available to the soil.
VERMICULITE	A water-absorbing substance made from mica. It is very useful for mixing with soil in pots and as a medium for growing seeds and cuttings, as it helps to hold water and air in the soil.

MEASUREMENTS IN THE GARDEN

We once had a very knowledgeable horticulture graduate working with us at our farm. She planned some very beautiful vegetable gardens which were weeded, dug over, composted and made ready for the big day of first planting. When I went into the garden to help, I found her planting beans with the aid of a tape measure. Well . . . to each his own, but I'm sure tape measures weren't invented when Adam was a boy, so the easy way to measure is to use the span of your hand (about 20cm/8in), the length of your top thumb-joint (about 2.5cm/1in), the length from your fingertip to your elbow (about 43cm/17in) or a big stride (about 80–90cm/3ft) as a guide. Your measurements would, of course, be different from mine but it really doesn't matter as plants can't read tape measures.

GARDEN EQUIPMENT

Buy the best you can afford.

- Fork
- Spade
- Shovel
- Plastic grass rake
- Metal rake
- Secateurs
- Trowel
- Hand fork
- Wheelbarrow
- Plastic buckets
- Selection of stakes
- Watering can
- Plastic garbage bins (for compost, liquid sprays and fertilisers)
- Craft/pop sticks for making rows of seeds, etc.
- Spray bottles
- Soft twine for tying up plants
- Garden sieve
- Garden hoses
- Gardening gloves
- Plastic pots
- Small jars for storing seeds
- Large jars for storing dried herbs
- Cheesecloth bags
- Old flyscreen windows for drying herbs
- Sharp garden knife and scissors
- Black plastic
- Fine-tip waterproof marker
- Selection of trays etc., for seed sowing

HELPING YOUR HERBS TO FLOURISH

The Herb Planting Chart (see pages 58–59) will give you some idea of the conditions under which your herbs will flourish. Please don't imagine that you have to avoid growing the plant if your soil doesn't conform to the suggestion given. This is a guide only to the most suitable conditions. Plants will, as a general rule, adapt to different soils and different amounts of sunlight; they will often tolerate some shade, even if they are specified as 'full sun' plants.

The amount of water needed is the condition which herbs seem least willing to change. Too much water on sage or lavender will cause them to die very quickly. Like a number of herbs, they hate having wet feet. If you deprive angelica or the mints of water, their growth will be very stunted or they will die. Try to arrange your garden so that plants which like plenty of water live together and the ones which enjoy drier conditions are in their own area.

HERB PLANTING CHART

B   Bottom heat needed to strike cuttings.

I   Invasive because they seed so readily. Create a corner to restrain or plant in large, deep containers. Easy to control by giving surplus plants away!

	Annual	Biennial	Perennial	Compact growth	Spreading habit	Frost-tender	Frost-resistant	Height, short—30cm (1ft)	Height, medium—90cm (3ft)	Height, tall—over 90cm (3ft)	Invasive—see above	Lots of water	Medium water	Little water	Grow from seed	Grow from cuttings	Grow from root division	Grow from mounding/layering	Grow from runners	Seeds may be sprouted	Soil, acid-loving	Semi-shade	Shade	Sun	Suitable for indoors	Winter dormant
ALFALFA			X	X			X		X				X							X						
ALOE			X	X		X			X					X			X							X	X	
ANGELICA		X		X			X		X				O										X			
ANISE	X			X	X			X					X	X										X		
BASIL	X			X	X	X							X	X										X	X	
BAY			X	X			X			X			X			B								X		
BERGAMOT			X	X	X	X		X					X			X		X		X						
BORAGE	X			X			X		X		I		X	X										X		
CALENDULA	X			X	X	X					I		X	X										X		
CARAWAY	X	X		X			X	X					X	X											X	
CATNEP			X	X			X	X					X		X	X	X							X		
CAYENNE		X		X	X			X					X	X										X		
CHAMOMILE, ROMAN			X		X	X		X					X			X		X				X	X			
CHAMOMILE, GERMAN	X			X	X			X					X	X										X		
CHICKWEED			X		X	X		X						X	X		X		X				X	X		
CHIVES			X	X			X	X					X											X	X	
COMFREY			X		X		X	X	X	X			X				X							X		X
CORIANDER	X			X	X			X					X	X										X		
DANDELION			X	X			X	X			I		X	X										X		
DILL	X			X	X			X					X	X										X		
ECHINACEA	X			X	X			X					X	X										X		X
ELDER			X	X			X			X			X		X									X		
FENNEL		X	X		X		X		X	X			X	X										X		
FEVERFEW			X	X			X	X			I		X	X										X		
GARLIC			X	X			X	X					X				X							X		
GINGER			X	X	X	X		X					X				X							X		
HORSERADISH			X	X	X		X	X	X				X				X							X		X
HYSSOP			X	X			X	X					X		X	X	X	X						X		
LANDCRESS		X		X		X	X				I	X		X						X				X		
LAVENDER			X	X			X	X						X	X	X		X						X		
LEMON BALM			X	X			X	X					X		X	X	X					X			X	

O Seed viable for a short time only.

W Collect from the wild if possible. Make sure the source is uncontaminated by traffic or chemical sprays.

	Annual	Biennial	Perennial	Compact growth	Spreading habit	Frost-tender	Frost-resistant	Height, short—30cm (1ft)	Height, medium—90cm (3ft)	Height, tall—over 90cm (3ft)	Invasive—see above	Lots of water	Medium water	Little water	Grow from seed	Grow from cuttings	Grow from root division	Grow from mounding/layering	Grow from runners	Grow from suckers	Seeds may be sprouted	Soil, acid-loving	Semi-shade	Shade	Sun	Suitable for indoors	Winter dormant
LEMON GRASS			X	X		X			X			X			X										X		
LIQUORICE			X		X	X			X	X			X		X			X							X		
MALLOW	X		X	X		X		X					X	X											X		
MARJORAM			X	X	X		X						X		X	X	X								X	X	
MINTS			X		X	X	X		X		X		X						X				X		X		
MULLEIN		X		X		X			X				X	X											X		
NASTURTIUM	X			X	X	X							X	X											X		
NETTLE	X		X		X	X	X				W	X	X	X											X		
OREGANO			X	X			X		X				X		X		X								X	X	
PARSLEY		X	X	X			X		X				X		X										X	X	
PENNYROYAL			X		X	X	X				X		X		X									X	X		
PLANTAIN			X	X		X		X			W	X	X	X											X		
RASPBERRY			X		X	X			X	X			X							X					X		
RED CLOVER			X	X		X			X				X		X						X				X		
ROSEMARY			X	X		X				X			X			X		X							X	X	
RUE			X	X		X			X				X	X	X										X		
SAGE			X	X		X	X						X	X	X										X		
SAVORY, SUMMER	X			X		X			X				X		X										X	X	
SAVORY, WINTER			X	X		X	X						X		X	X	X								X		
SHEPHERD'S PURSE	X			X		X	X	X			W	X	X	X											X		
SOUTHERNWOOD			X	X		X		X					X		X										X		
TANSY			X		X	X			X				X				X								X		
TARRAGON			X		X	X	X						X				X								X		X
THYME, GARDEN			X		X	X	X						X			X		X	X						X	X	
THYME, LEMON			X		X	X	X						X					X	X						X	X	
VALERIAN			X		X	X			X				X				X								X		X
VIOLET			X		X	X	X	X					X						X					X			
WATERCRESS			X		X	X	X				W	X							X		X	X	X		X		
WORMWOOD			X	X		X			X				X			X									X		
YARROW			X		X	X	X	X					X	X			X								X		
YELLOW DOCK			X		X	X			X		W	X	X	X											X		

GROWING HERBS FROM SEED

Seeds can be planted in containers and then transplanted, or sown directly in the garden where you want them to grow. The decision depends on several factors such as the size of seed, the difficulty of transplanting, and the weather conditions.

Assuming you are going to use trays, which is the safest way to be sure of raising a crop, you will need a bag of good quality potting mix or some sieved compost, and some seed trays. These need to be at least 3cm (1$\frac{1}{4}$in) high and have good drainage. Egg cartons make good seed trays as you can cut up the carton when the plant is 1–2cm (about $\frac{1}{2}$in) tall and plant each portion, complete with its little seedling, without disturbing the roots. The carton will rot, adding humus to the soil. I also use the little trays in which seedlings are sold, and other favourites of

mine are square 2 litre (3$\frac{1}{3}$ pint) ice cream containers. I cut these down to a suitable height and punch lots of holes in the bottom with a skewer. Things you would throw out as rubbish are often useful as seed trays.

Fill your container with potting mix and firm the surface to within 1cm ($\frac{1}{2}$in) of the top, water it down with Chamomile Spray (see Garden Sprays) and make drills (channels) in which to sow the seed. (If you are using egg cartons, the drills aren't necessary.) Sprinkle the seed as thinly as possible and cover with very finely sieved soil to about twice the thickness of the seed. If possible, place the tray in water when needed, rather than watering from above, as there is less chance of disturbing the seed. Occasionally, give a spray of chamomile to prevent 'damping off'.

The seed will need good light to germinate, but mustn't be left in full sun. A shadehouse or similar is ideal. The surface of the soil should never be allowed to dry out completely but neither should it be sodden, or the seeds or

Make drills and sow seeds

Cover seeds with finely sieved soil

Firm down gently with the back of your hand

Label the trays immediately using plastic tags and a waterproof pen

Thinning the seedlings

Transplanting the seedlings

seedlings will rot. You can cover the seed tray with a sheet of plastic or glass, removing it for an hour early morning and evening. This helps to prevent drying out and keeps the seeds warmer. The plastic or glass should be removed as soon as the plants show through.

The seedlings should be thinned out as soon as possible. Do this by nipping off surplus plants at surface level (choose the weaker ones, where possible) until there are no plants touching each other. Transplant when they are about 2–3cm ($^3/_4$–1$^1/_4$in) high, being very careful not to damage the delicate roots as you take them from the soil. I use a wooden tool shaped like a delicate, two-pronged fork, but a wooden craft or ice cream stick is fine. Water the hole before planting the seedling, and water again after planting. Gently firm the soil around the plant and finish with a dose of one of the garden sprays (see Garden Sprays) to ensure a good start.

GROWING HERBS FROM CUTTINGS

The advantage of growing a plant from a cutting is that you will get an exact replica of the parent, that is a 'clone'. The best time of day to take cuttings is in the early morning, before the sun has made the plant soft and limp. Winter is the best time of year to start cuttings of deciduous plants, and late spring for non-deciduous plants. Some plants are so obliging that any time seems all right. Sandy soil, river sand or vermiculite may be used to strike the cuttings. If you have problems striking your cuttings, you can buy a hormone powder (rooting powder), which can assist and hasten the growth of roots. Simply dip the fresh cutting into the powder, shake off the excess and plant as usual.

The best cuttings are 'heels'. These are small branches, pulled off gently downwards or cut with a sharp knife from the main stem of the parent plant. The next best are sprigs of about 10cm (4in) long, taken from the tip of a branch, cut on an angle, if possible, where there is a node (growing point). Trim the top leaves to half their length and strip the remaining leaves off the stem. Using a stick, make holes in the potting mixture (sandy soil, river sand or vermiculite), put the cuttings in the holes and firm in well, leaving about 5cm (2in) showing.

You can put a lot of cuttings in each pot – in fact, they seem to prefer this to being alone. When the pot is full, water it, put in a plastic bag in which you have punched 2 or 3 air holes and seal the top of the bag. Or place a plastic bag over the top and fasten with an elastic band. This stops the cuttings from drying out. Leave the pot in a semi-shaded position for 3–4 weeks, when the new plants should be ready to plant out. Open or remove the plastic bag every 3–4 days to give the plants some fresh air and prevent moulds from developing. Plant in the same way as seedlings, keeping the roots cool and moist.

Taking a heel cutting

Taking a tip cutting

Trimming at an angle, just below the node

Cut the top leaves back to half their length

Strip off the remaining leaves

Cuttings enclosed in a plastic bag greenhouse

I live on sandy soil and often put cuttings straight in the ground where they are to grow. I cover them with a plastic bag with some holes punched in it, weigh the edges down with stones or rocks and leave it on until I see some new top growth. Take the bag off for about an hour, three times a week, to give a good airing to the plant. them out of the pot.

PROPAGATING HERBS

ROOT DIVISION

The best time for this method of propagation is early spring, when the new growth is just beginning to appear. It is not only desirable but necessary to divide perennials, as it gives them a new lease on life and prevents clumps from becoming too big and straggly.

This is a really easy way to grow new plants.

Simply lift the whole clump and pull or cut it into new plants, each one having its own piece of root. Trim the tops and roots back equally to avoid stress to the new plant. Replant as quickly as possible and water in very well. If for some reason you can't plant immediately, be sure to cover the roots with a wet sack or cloth to prevent them from drying out.

Some plants, particularly comfrey and horseradish, can be propagated by chopping their roots into several parts (each part must have an 'eye'). These separate pieces of root will each grow into a plant.

Comfrey

Using a spade, divide a tough clump of roots

Pulling a clump of roots apart

Mounding a plant with soil

Freeing the tips of a mounded plant

Using a peg to layer a branch

PROPAGATING HERBS BY MOUNDING

Some plants may be very easily propagated by mounding. The best time to do this is in autumn. The plant is mounded over with soil and then shaken lightly to enable the soil to get right down among the branches. About 12–15cm (5–6in) of the top of the plant must be left exposed. Leave the plant over winter, topping up with soil if needed. In spring, lift the whole plant and, with secateurs, cut away all the new rooted cuttings.

Covering the pegged area with soil

Mounding is a good system to use with plants which have become leggy and bare at the base – thyme, lavender, small rosemaries and winter savory are some of the plants which benefit from being treated in this way.

PROPAGATING HERBS BY LAYERING

This is similar to mounding, but only single stems are treated.

Pegs are needed to hold the stem or branch on the ground and all but the tip is covered with soil. After a few weeks the soil may be removed and the rooted stem cut away from the main plant. The pegs may be pieces of wire about 10cm (4in) long and bent into a peg shape.

GROWING HERBS INDOORS

It's possible to grow some herbs in pots, either indoors or out. Herbs which can be grown this way are indicated in the Herb Planting Chart. The soil used is most important, as it needs to retain plenty of moisture but also to drain well. I use half-and-half compost and sandy loam. The sandy loam could be replaced by a bought potting mix. Choose your potting mix carefully as some brands are much better than others. If you have a good nursery nearby, take the advice of the owner or gardener and then buy a small bag to start with.

Herbs grown indoors never seem to get as big or strong as those grown in the garden. Let's face it, there is no such thing as an indoor plant. There are only plants which will tolerate being indoors or which need to be wintered indoors because they are not in their native habitat. With all this in mind it is worth a try. Some people

have more success than others when growing herbs indoors.

The prime requirements are good light (but not burning heat through glass), fresh air without a draught, and not much artificial heat. Try to give them a day every now and again in a sheltered place out of doors.

COMPOST

Now that you are growing your herbs you will be wondering how to fertilise them. Compost and herbal sprays, if well made, are the only nutrition they will ever need. Compost is a home-made fertiliser made from rotted organic ingredients. It is cheap, natural and adds humus to the soil. It improves drainage in a heavy soil and holds moisture in a sandy or light soil. None of these advantages is to be gained by using any of the artificial fertilisers.

If you are trying to avoid the use of chemicals or other pollutants in your garden, you should be very careful about the raw materials you use in the compost heap. The fragrant grass clippings from your local lawn-mowing man could well be from lawns which have been sprayed with weed-killers or other poisons. The rich, wholesome looking animal manure you buy from a farmer may be from animals which have been treated with antibiotics or chemical drenches. Seaweed washed up after a storm may contain heavy metals or other undesirable elements introduced into the ocean from factory effluent or ships. There is no need to become paranoid about this problem but you should maintain an awareness and ask potential suppliers what, if anything, has been used. It has been my experience that no offence is caused if the questions are asked diplomatically. In fact, the people concerned show a great deal of interest, as it frequently hasn't occurred to them that the recycling of these raw materials could cause a problem.

If you become a 'compost addict' (a very easy addiction to form) there are many books available on compost-making. I am a rather lazy gardener and an impatient one as well so I look for both the quickest and the easiest way. The methods which follow have been working well for me for many years.

AEROBIC COMPOSTING

In this method, the heap is turned regularly, allowing oxygen into the mix to speed up the decomposition process and keep the compost smelling sweet. If an aerobic heap smells nasty or isn't heating up, then it's not working properly and you need to consider what you may be doing wrong. It could be too much or too little water or sun, not enough nitrogenous matter (such as manure or grass clippings), or you may not be turning it enough. The most common error is overwatering. This is easily rectified by adding more dry material, such as sawdust or straw.

Collect the materials in separate piles or bins. Use grass clippings, manure (dog and cat manure is okay if left to mature for a long time), weeds, leaves (preferably from deciduous trees), food scraps, vacuum-cleaner contents, hair, hay, straw, sawdust to name just a few. Avoid adding fat as it takes a long time to decompose. The finer all the materials are, the quicker the compost pile will be complete and ready to use.

When you have enough, choose a partly shaded area near to a tap, (filtered light under a tree is ideal) and not too close to the house. I arrange for lawn clippings and horse manure to be delivered on the same day if possible. All household scraps and green waste from my garden have been accumulating in bins with some soil sprinkled over to deter marauding animals. When everything is ready, plus a bag of garden lime to sweeten the pile, I can begin.

This method has the advantage of not using bins as the basis of its construction but it could

Herbs on the compost heap

make a neat, small garden look a bit messy. This may not bother you if, like me, you are so proud of your compost that guests in their 'glad rags' are led down the garden path to admire the compost heap before they get to eat!

BUILDING A COMPOST HEAP

1. Dig over the soil and insert a central pole for aeration and watering.
2. Put a layer of loose material (such as leaves) to assist aeration.
3. Spread a 5cm (2in) thick layer of manure.
4. Sprinkle over a small handful of lime.
5. Put on 30cm (12in) grass clippings, vegetable scraps or other organic waste, plus finely chopped herbs (see page 68).
6. Cover with 2–3cm ($^3/_4$–$1^1/_4$in) of soil.

Repeat these layers until the pile is 1–2m ($3^1/_4$–$6^1/_2$ft) high, finishing with a thicker layer of soil. The minimum size for a heap is 1m x 1m ($3^1/_4$ft x $3^1/_4$ft). Any smaller and it won't heat up. Try to have the base of the pile the same size as the height for optimum efficiency. Remove the stake and water the pile. It is impossible to tell you how much water to add. The pile needs to be as moist as a squeezed-out sponge.

Cover with a sheet of black plastic with a few holes punched in and weight this down with rocks or bricks. During the next week turn the pile twice. Have an identical patch dug next to it ready for turning the pile onto, and then watch it go. It will begin to heat up very quickly and it is possible for a heap to reach a temperature of 75°C (167°F) which will kill disease organisms and seeds. Don't forget to keep it moist. After the first two weeks, turn only about once weekly.

After about two weeks the pile will have cooled and it is at this stage that you add the final touch to give you a perfect compost heap. Poke holes in the pile and introduce as many worms as you can beg, borrow or buy. They will do miraculous things in a very short time. They chew up the raw materials and pass them out the other end as fine castings full of nitrogen, phosphorus, potassium, magnesium and calcium. Look in your local telephone directory for 'Worm Farms' and the owners will be able to advise you how many you will need. If the materials were finely cut and the weather is warm, you should have compost in about 6 weeks. The pile will end up about a quarter of its original size.

USING COMPOST BINS

If you want aesthetically pleasing bins, you can make wooden ones. If, however, the bin area is out of sight and you are looking, like me, at 'recycled, quick and cheap', you can use any discarded, non-absorbent building materials, such as corrugated iron, plastic or plywood.

It is good to have two or even three bins side by side, so that the mix can be turned from one into the other with the minimum of labour.

I tend to have both a compost heap and compost bins. The heap seems to be a little quicker, but the bins are useful for sorting and storing while you are waiting to accumulate sufficient materials and they keep your compost in one place if you aren't going to use it all at once.

This compost is what you are going to use for potting and to pile on your garden, adding humus and nutrients to the soil and plants. It is the only fertiliser, humus and mulch you will need, apart from herbal sprays.

I think we need to be thankful that composting methods have changed over the years. The recipe which follows doesn't appeal to me at all!

Compost

2 Barrowsful of goose dung, steeped in bullocks blood
2 Barrowsful of sugar-bakers scum
2 Barrowsful of night soil
2 Barrowsful of fine yellow loam

– ISAAC EMMERTON, CULTURE AND MANAGEMENT OF THE AURICULA, 1815

Herbs to use in the Compost Heap

There are several herbs which will enrich your compost when added to the mix:

COMFREY: Adds calcium, nitrogen, potassium.

YARROW: One chopped leaf in each layer will accelerate the pile. Yarrow contains copper, nitrates and phosphates.

NETTLE: Adds iron, copper and calcium.

DANDELION: Adds iron, copper, potassium, sulfur and manganese.

CHAMOMILE: 'Sweetens' the pile, rich in calcium.

You need not restrict yourself to these herbs but they are very rich in the minerals needed, although all herbs will add vital nutrients. I often trim the herbs and scatter the clippings directly onto the garden to rot. They act as mulch, humus and fertiliser.

Biodynamic Herbal Fertiliser

Versions of this fertiliser are widely used with very successful results. It is best to use dried herbs, but if you can, use double the quantity of fresh if dried are not available. Spray or water this solution on to your garden every two weeks during spring and autumn.

1 teaspoon cow or horse manure, dried
1 cup each chamomile, dandelion leaves, nettle,
plantain, sage and yarrow
water

Mix the manure well with 5 litres (about 1 gallon) water and leave in the sun for 2 days.

To 1 cup of this liquid, add the herbs plus 22 litres (about 5 gallons) water. Leave in the sun for a further 2 days. Strain before using.

If you don't need the remaining manure liquid for further treatments, you can pour it over your compost heap, along with the strained herbs.

RIGHT: *Herbs scattered over the compost heap to add extra nutrients to the compost*

SOME SUGGESTIONS
FOR GARDEN PLANNING

HERBS LOVED BY BEES AND BUTTERFLIES

Plant these throughout your vegetable garden, under fruit trees or anywhere that you want good pollination to take place.

Anise	**Basil**	**Mallow**	**Marjoram**
Bergamot	**Borage**	**Mints**	**Rosemary**
Catnep	**Dandelion**	**Sage**	**Thyme**
Lavender	**Lemon Balm**	**Valerian**	**Yarrow**

Colour in the Garden

If you want to create drama in the garden it can often be achieved quite easily by solid plantings of one herb or herbs of the same colour or shades of that colour. Too many colours in one area can be distracting to the eye – imagine a slope, misty with the mauves and purples of thymes at the base, hyssop or violets a little higher and lavenders curving around the rise and standing tall above.

For a vibrant range of yellows and oranges, plant nasturtiums at the front, calendulas behind and tansy at the back of a bed or border. A tepee bearing climbing beans can be a glorious centre-piece for the garden especially with nasturtiums twining and blossoming around the base.

A bed of tomatoes, calendulas and parsley is a feast for the eye as well as for the stomach.

The silver-grey herbs provide a striking background for red and pink herbs such as bergamot, red yarrow and valerian.

The white herbs can create restful areas between blocks of colour or subtle shading to break up a too rampant display of bold shades.

The Herb Planting Chart, Herbs For Colour and Companion Planting Chart will help you to plan colour in your garden by matching herbs and vegetables by height, water/sun and companionship requirements.

HERBS FOR COLOUR

Grey or Silver Herbs

Catnep

Sage

Lavender

Southernwood

Rue

Wormwood

Red/Pink Flowers

Bergamot

Coriander

Valerian

Clover

Mallow

Yarrow

Comfrey

Savory, Summer

Blue, Mauve Or Purple Flowers

Borage

Hyssop

Rosemary

Catnep

Lavender

Thyme

Chives

Pennyroyal

Violet

Yellow/Orange Flowers

Aloe

Dill

Calendula

Nasturtium

Tansy

Dandelion

Rue

To create drama in the garden, plant one herb or herbs of the same colour or shades of that colour. Imagine a slope, misty with the mauves and purples of thymes at the base, hyssop or violets a little higher and lavenders standing tall above.

White Flowers

Anise
Catnep
Feverfew
Basil
Chamomile
Lemon Balm
Caraway
Elder
Marjoram
Savory, Winter
Yarrow

Aromatic Herbs

Angelica
Catnep
Lavender
Mint
Tansy
Basil
Chamomile
Lemon Balm
Rosemary
Thyme
Bergamot
Coriander
Marjoram
Southernwood
Wormwood

Flowers for Salads

Bergamot
Dandelion
Nasturtium
Borage
Elder
Rosemary
Calendula
Fennel
Violet

COMPANION PLANTING

It is well known that some plants like or dislike each other. The reasons for these preferences are many and sometimes it's impossible to know why they exist.

Companion planting in the vegetable garden

Some plants exude such strong essential oil perfumes that they disguise the smell of other neighbouring plants, thus protecting the plants from predators. Other herbs give off secretions from their roots which benefit nearby plants, or their roots penetrate the soil to such a depth that nutrients are brought into the upper soil. These deep-rooted plants have the additional benefit of helping to break up heavy soil. Tall plants protect smaller plants from wind and sun. Some plants are visited by bees and other insects, thus helping to attract pollinating insects to the vicinity.

A lot of companion planting is plain common sense, part of knowing your herbs and what conditions they like. You may make mistakes initially but these mistakes are sometimes the best way of learning. I make every effort not to move self-sown plants, which often appear, seemingly from nowhere, in my garden. These plants are almost always stronger and bigger than the plants which I put into the ground with such care! When I go for walks, I find it of great interest to see where plants choose to grow in the wild. I learn a lot from these observations.

The average garden is a far cry from the forests of Europe, the dry, hot cliffs of Greece or the lush meadows and hedgerows of Britain. The best we can do is to be as sensitive as possible to these plants and their needs. They will repay us many times over for our efforts.

COMPANION PLANTING

PLANT	GOOD COMPANION	BAD COMPANION
APPLE TREES	Chives, horseradish, garlic, nasturtium, tansy	
APRICOT TREES	Basil, horseradish, southernwood, tansy	
ASPARAGUS	Anise, basil, parsley	
BEANS, ALL	Anise, calendula, savory	Fennel, garlic
BROCCOLI	Anise, nasturtium, thyme	
BRUSSELS SPROUTS	Anise, chamomiles, coriander, dill, hyssop, mint, nasturtium, oregano, rosemary, sage, tansy, thyme	Garlic, rue
CAULIFLOWER	Anise, nasturtium, tansy, thyme	
CARROTS	Anise, chives, coriander, rosemary, sage	
CELERY	Anise, dill	
CUCUMBER	Anise, chives, marjoram, nasturtium, oregano	
GRAPES	Basil, hyssop, nasturtium, tansy	
LETTUCE	Anise, calendula	
PARSNIPS	Anise, garlic	
PEACH TREES	Garlic, nasturtium, tansy	
POTATOES	Calendula, horseradish	Rosemary
RADISHES	Anise, nasturtium	Hyssop
RASPBERRIES	Tansy	
ROSES	Calendula, chives, garlic, parsley, tansy	
SILVERBEET	Anise, lavender	
STRAWBERRIES	Anise, borage, sage	Garlic
TOMATOES	Anise, basil, calendula, chives dill, parsley	Fennel, rosemary
ZUCCHINI	Anise, nasturtium	

INSECT REPELLENT HERBS

The term 'insect repellent' is rather misleading as it suggests the aim of the gardener is to rid the garden of insects. What a disaster that would be! Pollination would slow down dramatically if there was just the wind to rely on. I suppose, if we are truthful about what we really want, we are asking for the pest-free garden, undamaged fruit and vegetables, aphis-free roses and baby plants growing free from the threat of slugs and snails – all this without resorting to the use of any poisonous sprays.

What we need to aim for is not to kill insects but to discourage them from destroying the plants. This can be achieved with time, effort, a few 'tricks' and a lot of herbs.

Snails and slugs are a real threat only to young seedlings and these are fairly easy to protect. I cut and discard the bottoms out of a number of plant pots, push these into the soil around each young plant and remove them only when the plant is well established. They get plenty of light and seem to appreciate the protection, not only from snails but from wind. Fresh grass clippings or wood cinders around young plants also deters snails as well as providing mulch to keep their tender roots as cool as possible.

Some herbs can be used to repel certain insects. This is not going to work if you plant one solitary basil near a rose bush and trust that every aphid in the vicinity is going to leave. You need to plant enough of the herb you have chosen to form a reasonable barrier near the plant you want to protect. For instance, if a border of feverfew is planted around a bed of carrots, the strong scent will mask the smell of the carrots and the carrot fly will fly over your garden to your next-door neighbour's.

I have noticed that self-sown plants are rarely bothered by insects or disease. There is a valuable lesson to be learnt here. A strong, healthy plant, growing in the right position, in good soil, can put up its own resistance. If you want a good vegetable garden, you need to avoid growing crops in the same position more than once every four years. This is known as crop rotation. It has the double benefit of discouraging insect pests from reaching plague proportions by breeding in the same patch while preventing the ground from being depleted of the particular nutrients taken from it by that crop.

Some herbs are of general benefit and protection to plants. It's good to plant these among your vegetables and flowers and also to use them in sprays. For very large gardens, you may need a large sprayer but for smaller gardens a small spray bottle will often do. This can be a recycled, well-washed kitchen or bathroom cleanser bottle, with a spray nozzle on it.

I'm afraid, however, that there will always be an ongoing battle with the snails. My father used the 'torch and gumboot' deterrent for snails. You wait till evening (moist if possible), put on gumboots, grab a torch, go into the garden and stamp on snails!

INSECT REPELLENT CHART

Interplant or surround the garden bed with the recommended insect-repellent herb
to mask the odour of the plants you wish to protect.

INSECT	INSECT-REPELLENT HERBS
ANTS	Marjoram, mint, oregano, pennyroyal, rue, tansy
APHIS	Basil, caraway, chives, coriander, elder, nasturtium, tansy
APPLE SCAB	Chives, horseradish
BEETLES	Catnep, lavender, nasturtium, rosemary, tansy, wormwood
BLACK FLY	Thyme
CABBAGE MOTH	Coriander, dill
CABBAGE WORM	Chamomile, coriander
CARROT FLY	Coriander, rosemary, sage, wormwood
CATERPILLARS	Elder, mint
EELWORM	Calendula
FLEAS	Fennel, pennyroyal, rosemary, rue, tansy
FLIES	Basil, caraway, lavender, rue
FUNGUS	Chamomile
MICE	Catnep, mint, tansy
MOSQUITOES	Basil, caraway, elder, feverfew, garlic, pennyroyal
MOTHS	Bay, chamomile, feverfew, tansy
SNAILS AND SLUGS	Horseradish, pennyroyal, rue, sage, wormwood
SILVERFISH	Bay, tansy, wormwood
WEEVILS	Bay

There are a few herbs which offer general benefits and protection:
ANISE, FEVERFEW, GARLIC, HYSSOP, SOUTHERNWOOD, YARROW: Give general protection to most plants.
BORAGE: Increases resistance to disease.
LEMON BALM, NETTLE: Use in general-purpose sprays.

GARDEN SPRAYS

Chamomile Spray

Make a Triple Strength Infusion. Stand for 24 hours. Strain, dilute to a weak tea. Use to give a lift to sick plants or water onto young seedlings to prevent 'damping off'.

Elderflower Spray

Make a Triple Strength Infusion. Stand for 24 hours. Strain, dilute to a weak tea. Spray on young plants to protect from insects and caterpillars.

Garlic Spray

100g (3¹/₂oz) garlic cloves
6 onions
6 red chillies
paraffin oil to cover
4 cups (1 litre/1³/₄ pints) water
1 cup (100g/3¹/₂oz) skim dried milk powder

Blend garlic, onion and chillies well. Add, paraffin oil and leave to stand for 2 days.

Add water and skim milk powder and mix well, then strain through a fine cloth.

Dilute 1 part spray to 50 parts water (stronger if needed) and use to spray against aphis, ants, spiders, caterpillars.

Nettle Spray

Cover nettles with water, put lid on container and leave until rotted and fermenting. Strain before use. Nettles add valuable vitamins and minerals to the soil.

General Spray

Use southernwood, mint, tansy, feverfew, chamomile, nettle, parsley, sage and borage.

Mix equal quantities of as many as possible of these herbs together and make as for nettle spray. This will repel insects and give health to plants.

GATHERING HERBS

Herbs love being picked and will grow much better if 'pruned' regularly. The difference to the taste buds between shop-bought dried herbs and your own carefully dried or freshly picked herbs is very pronounced. You also have the satisfaction of knowing that they are as uncontaminated as you could possibly manage to make them.

To ensure a regular supply of herbs you will need to harvest and preserve your own as they reach their peak. This is usually just as they come into flower.

Choose a warm, sunny morning to harvest – before the sun is too strong, but after every trace of moisture has dried from the plant. The picking time is critical as the sun causes the plant to 'expire' its precious essential oils. These oils are what gives the plant most of its perfume and flavour and must be protected at every stage, from picking to using.

GATHERING LEAVES

Cut a whole branch or stem just as the plant is coming into flower, cutting the stem just on or above a leaf node. Take only as much as you can process quickly, as the leaves can deteriorate very soon after picking. Pick over the material, discarding all dead or discoloured parts. It's pointless storing anything but the best.

GATHERING FLOWERS

Cut these just before they are most fully open.

PICKING SEEDS

Cut whole heads as they turn beige to brown. If there is a danger of the seed falling before you gather it, the head may be enclosed in a paper or muslin bag until the seeds are ripe (see Drying Herbs).

GATHERING ROOTS

The roots are usually collected in the plant's most dormant season when there is not much leaf growth.

DRYING HERBS

The quicker you dry your herbs, the better the colour and flavour will be. However, they must never be dried in direct sunlight or high temperatures as this destroys the plant's special properties.

Choose an airy, dust-free area or an oven set at its lowest temperature, with the door open. Keep the herbs low down in the oven and turn them regularly. If you have a wood stove in your kitchen, you can create a wonderful drying area by making screen racks to fit above the stove. This is the method we used most at our farm as it could be utilised all year round.

Manufacturers maintain that herbs can be dried using microwave ovens. I feel that while the plants may dry satisfactorily, the essential oils may be lost. These oils are very sensitive to heat and need to be treated with the utmost respect. I would therefore hesitate to recommend this form of drying.

An electric dehydrator is excellent for drying herbs but be sure to buy a model with a fan for circulating air and also a temperature control which can be set to about 35°C (95°F) – this may sound hot but as there is air circulating constantly, the herbs stay cool.

LEAVES AND FLOWERS

These can be tied in small bunches and hung in a suitable area. If dust or flies are a problem, enclose the bunches in muslin bags. They can be spread on insect screens or dried in the oven as described above. If liked, the leaves may be stripped from the stems. The material is dry when it is just becoming crisp. If you are using an oven, watch the herbs carefully to prevent overdrying.

ROOTS, BARK AND STEMS

These parts of the plant usually need to be washed and thoroughly dried, then chopped as finely as possible to speed up the drying process. I find the oven method best for roots but, unlike leaves and flowers, roots may be dried in the sun.

If you are doing them in summer, spread them on old flyscreens or some other suitable type of mesh, cover them with cheesecloth and put them in a sunny place away from dust. (On top of a water tank or shadehouse will do.) Roots, bark and stems are dry when they snap easily.

SEEDS

The best way to dry seeds is to cut the whole seed-heads off, enclose them in a muslin or cheese-cloth bag, hang them in an airy place and forget them for about two months. If you prefer, you can strip the seeds off the heads first. Do search the seed heads for insects first or you may have provided a tasty larder for creepies!

LARGE LEAVES AND PODS

The way to deal easily with large leaves such as borage, comfrey and mullein, and with pods such as chillies, is to thread a large needle with tough linen thread or dental floss and push the needle through the stem of the leaf or pod. Hang them in such a way that they won't touch each other.

STORAGE

Over the years I have experimented with several methods of storage and have finally settled on glass jars. These give protection from damp, insects and dust and have the advantage of allowing you to keep a close eye on the contents. It's very important to check the jars regularly, particularly in the first few weeks, as any moisture left in the herbs could cause mould to develop.

Try to choose a jar which fits the amount of herb. A lot of air in the jar will detract from the keeping qualities of the herbs being stored. Collect sizes from very large to very small. Label your jars very carefully with the common name, Latin name and the date of storage. Don't trust your memory, as many herbs smell and look very similar after they are dried.

CHAPTER THREE

HERBS THAT HEAL

Herbs can play a great part in keeping us healthy but, no matter

how much care we take, accidents sometimes happen or we become

stressed and succumb to illness. Herbs will support and help your

body to rally its defences and can also be powerfully curative.

In this chapter you will find charts which will help you to treat adults

and children suffering from simple everyday complaints and help you

deal with emergency situations. However, if a problem is serious or

of long duration you would be wise to seek the help of a professional

who will respect your desire to use the most holistic and natural

treatments and who will also act in an advisory manner, guiding you

to the best treatment for your particular problem.

This chapter concerns illness or disease and the part which herbs play in restoring health to the body and mind. Unlike many modern drugs which aim a 'bullet' at a symptom, herbs work in quite a different way by helping the body to rally its defences and regain its balance. The written records of the use of herbs for healing go back about 2000 years. Who knows how far back in time the unrecorded use stretches? Many of the remedies are the same now as then, and I find it awe-inspiring that they should have survived such a test of time. People who deny the value of herbs are those who have either never tried them, or who drank one cup of herb tea and complained that their problem was still with them.

Humans have been slowly evolving over millions of years. For most of this time it has been a natural, unforced, unhurried process, allowing plenty of time for the planet and its inhabitants to adapt to changing conditions. Nature uses floods, famine, plague and predators as natural selectors to ensure the survival of the fittest.

In the last 50 years this situation has changed radically. I was a nurse in the mid-1940s when penicillin was introduced. Tuberculosis, pneumonia and many other diseases

which had been difficult to cure ceased to be a threat. The sulpha drugs appeared in the early 1950s and brought more diseases under control. What has happened? We live longer and many life-threatening diseases can be overcome but we are no healthier – in fact, we appear to have exchanged one set of problems for new and possibly more dangerous ones, such as AIDS.

Along with the discovery of the 'wonder drugs' came the pesticides, herbicides, hormone treatments for animals, artificial fibres, aerosol cans full of insecticides and oven cleaners, air pollution from an increasing number of factories and vehicles – the list grows alarmingly. Add to this the increasing migration of humans from town to town and country to country and you have a situation where we are unable to adapt sufficiently quickly. Had these changes happened over thousands of years we might have changed with them but our abused autoimmune systems, subjected to chemicals, the overuse of antibiotics, and new climates and pollens, have become confused and given up the unequal battle. AIDS, allergies and candida albicans are some of the illnesses resulting from this breakdown.

What can we do about this situation? We can take preventive measures by making our homes and gardens 'toxic-free zones' and take as much responsibility as possible for our health. We need to learn to be confident in our own capabilities and intelligence. I must say at this point that I am not in any way condemning the medical profession or drugs. I know many dedicated, open-minded doctors who are beginning to look at alternative methods with great interest and who try to restrict the use of drugs (it's the overuse of drugs that creates the problem). I have also had experience of charlatans in the alternative fields of healing, who seem to be in the profession merely to make money. The blame can be laid squarely at our own doorstep. Every time we place the responsibility for our well-being on someone else, we are weakening ourselves.

The role of health professionals, as I see it, is to use their diagnostic skills to determine the nature of the problem, attempt to find the underlying cause, and then suggest a course of treatment. The role of the patient is to ask questions and to be prepared to change a lifestyle if necessary, rather than hold out a hand for a bottle of

pills. It's not easy to change the living patterns of a lifetime but this is frequently the only way to get the body into a state of 'ease' rather than 'dis-ease'.

It's to be hoped that the next few years will see more of a 'marriage' between allopathic and alternative styles of medicine, each giving of its best to create truly holistic methods of healing.

This chapter is not intended to be an instant medical 'self-help guide'. The correct use of herbs can be complex and you need guidance from as many reliable sources as you can find. Establish a firm relationship with a reputable herbalist, naturopath, homeopath, doctor or other health professional who will respect your view and, until you have had a great deal of experience with herbs, rely on the experience of your chosen therapist to guide you.

The best way to learn about herbs is first to grow them, learning all you can about each one and the way they react with each other. Become accustomed to sharing your life with herbs, using them in as many ways as possible – the chances are you will be so healthy you might never need this chapter!

EQUIPMENT

Keep separate equipment for making all your recipes. Some things become discoloured or impregnated with the perfume of herb oils, tinctures and teas, and would be unsuitable for use in cooking food. Most of these items are not expensive and can usually be picked up for cents at second-hand shops or sales.

2 teaspoons

2 tablespoons

wooden spoons

1 or 2 funnels

coffee filter papers

scales

droppers

sharp knife

scissors

2 sieves, different sizes

2 or 3 measuring jugs

2 or 3 bowls, different sizes

25ml plastic measure

mortar and pestle or coffee grinder

2 or 3 saucepans, different sizes, made of glass, steel or unchipped enamel, not aluminium. One pan or bowl should fit neatly into another pan to create a double boiler.

Cheesecloth (fine, unbleached) for making bags and for the fine straining. It's a good idea to make several different-sized bags, varying in size from 8 x 12cm (3 x 5in) up to 18 x 25cm (7 x 10in). I use double-thickness cheesecloth and make the bags with French seams for strength.

screw-top jars, different sizes and sterilised

labels

waterproof marking pen, fine tip

clean, old tea towels

If you get really involved in making a lot of the recipes you will need heat-resistant-glass measuring flasks. These are expensive and can be added one at a time as the need arises.

HERBAL PREPARATION METHODS

Measurements in this book are based on metric spoons, so:

18–20 drops = 1ml

90–100 drops = 5ml (^{1}⁄$_6$fl oz) = 1 teaspoon

1 Australian tablespoon = 20ml (^{2}⁄$_3$fl oz)

INFUSIONS: Mixtures made by pouring boiling water over herbs and leaving them to stand for 5–10 minutes.

DECOCTIONS: Mixtures made by simmering the herbs in water for up to half an hour.

TINCTURES: Alcoholic extracts of herbs, made by steeping the herbs in alcohol for about 2 weeks.

INFUSION OR TEA

This is the simplest and most widely used preparation, particularly for the 'beginner herbalist'. This method is used for ground roots and bark, crushed seeds and finely chopped flowers and leaves. Infusions and decoctions are the most suitable preparations to give to children. Your herbal preparations deserve their own special, scrupulously clean, non-metal pot or teapot (aluminium or the flavour of ordinary tea can taint the delicate taste of infusions).

Infusions can be used in several ways. The most obvious is for drinking, but by making it up at 3 or 4 times the usual concentration, your infusion will be strengthened for use in baths, fomentations, compresses, poultices and ointments.

To Make an Infusion or Tea

For a normal strength infusion (or tea), pour 1 cup (250ml/8fl oz) boiling water over 2 heaped teaspoons finely chopped fresh herbs, or 1 heaped teaspoon crumbled dried herb. Cover and stand for 5–10 minutes; strain and sweeten with honey if you wish.

It is important to cover the hot infusion to prevent the precious essential oils escaping, which robs the preparation of much of its healing potential.

Triple Strength Infusion or Decoction

Make as for a normal strength infusion or decoction using triple the amount of herbs with the 1 cup (250ml/8fl oz) water.

Dosage

Adults: $^1/_2$ cup (125ml/4fl oz) 3 times daily, $^1/_2$ hour before food.

Children: 30kg (66lb) plus   half adult dose
       15–29kg (33–64lb)   quarter adult dose
       7–14kg (15–31lb)   eighth adult dose

DECOCTIONS

Some plants need to be simmered to extract their properties. Roots and barks are the parts usually treated in this way. Before beginning the decoction, chop the material as finely as possible. This is difficult with some dried roots and barks, but you can resort to a cleaver if necessary.

To Make a Decoction

To each 1 cup (250ml/8fl oz) cold water add 2 teaspoons fresh or 1 teaspoon dried herbs. Bring to the boil, cover and simmer for 10–30 minutes, depending on the fineness of the material. Strain and make up to the original 1 cup (250ml/8fl oz) with fresh boiling water. The best way to make a decoction is to invest in a crock-pot or slow-cooker. The decoction can be left covered for several hours, gradually releasing the herbal properties and retaining the maximum amount of its potency. Sufficient quantity for several days can be made at once by this method. It should be kept in a covered container in a refrigerator and used within 4–5 days.

TINCTURES

A tincture is an alcoholic extract of herbs. Tinctures are stronger and more concentrated than infusions or decoctions. You can make them in advance and, if well made and stored, they will keep for years.

The keeping qualities of the tincture are largely determined by the strength of the alcohol you use. Pure alcohol is usually only available to professional users but occasionally you will find a pharmacist who will sell you 95% alcohol. You will need to dilute this with purified water until it is 60%. Otherwise, rely on your wine and spirit merchant to advise you on the highest proof vodka, gin or brandy he has in stock.

To Make a Tincture

While some recommend determining the amount of herb to use by its weight, I have found that its density can be more reliable. For example, 125g (4oz) comfrey root is quite a small amount in volume, while 125g (4oz) calendula petals is a large amount which may not be covered by the amount of alcohol specified. You should find this method gives you a very fine tincture.

LEAVES AND FLOWERS – FRESH OR DRIED:
Loosely fill a jar with the finely chopped fresh herbs or half fill if the material is dried. Cover the herbs with alcohol and close the jar with a well-fitting lid.

ROOTS, BARK AND SEEDS:
Cover 30g (1oz) herb, depending on density, with 250ml (1 cup) alcohol. Mark the jar (not the lid) with the common and Latin name of the plant

and the date two weeks hence. This is when the tincture will be ready. Keep the tinctures where you can see them, so you can tend them twice a day. To do this, fold a cloth and place it on the bench. Then tap the jar base gently but firmly on the cloth for at least one minute. This process, called 'succussion', releases the medicinal properties from the herb into the alcohol.

After 2 weeks the tincture is ready to be strained through a coffee filter into a dark-coloured glass bottle, labelled with the name, Latin name, date and the symbol Ø, which denotes that it is a Mother Tincture. Store the bottle in a cool dark place and it should last for years. If you like, you can add 1 teaspoon glycerine to each 1 cup (250ml/8fl oz) tincture to help it keep well.

Uses and Dosages of Tinctures

INTERNAL: 5–15 drops taken in 2 tablespoons milk or water 3 times a day before meals, or added, 5 drops at a time, to infusions and decoctions to strengthen their action. 1 teaspoon of tincture is equivalent in action and strength to 1 cup of infusion or decoction. For further information on internal use refer to Healthy Remedies chart.

EXTERNAL: Tinctures may be added to poultices, fomentations, compresses, ointments, wound washes and anywhere you may want to increase the strength of the remedy. They may be used undiluted where needed in order to quickly stop infection or bleeding.

SYRUPS

These are used to disguise unpleasant-tasting herbs, or when a cough or sore throat syrup is needed.

To Make a Syrup

In a non-aluminium pan combine 500g (1lb) of sugar and 1 cup (250ml/8fl oz) of water. Heat, stirring, until the sugar is dissolved and the liquid is boiling. Remove from the heat, cool, bottle and store in the refrigerator.

To Use a Syrup

To each 3 parts syrup, add 1 part tincture; or to each 3 parts syrup add 1 part Triple Strength Infusion or decoction.
Dose: 20–60 drops as needed, according to age.

OXYMEL

Oxymel is a honey mixture, which can be used instead of syrup to flavour herbal medicines. While it is just as bad for your teeth as sugar (you need to clean your teeth after taking any sweetened preparations) some people prefer honey for its flavour and its own medicinal properties.

To Make an Oxymel

Boil 5 parts honey and 1 part cider vinegar to a thick syrup, taking care not to let it burn. Cool and use it in the same way as syrup.

EAR TREATMENTS

Ear pain must always be taken very seriously, especially in a child. It can be a symptom of middle ear infection, mastoiditis or other complaints which need treatment by a professional. Untreated ear problems can lead to partial or complete hearing loss. If you are consulting professionals, whether herbalists or conventional doctors, it is important to tell them what, if any, herbal remedies you are already using, in case this might have a bearing on the suggested treatment.

Some mild ear problems can be dealt with successfully at home, especially if there is no severe pain. Dry eczema, excess wax and outer ear infections are some of the problems which can be dealt with very effectively by the use of garlic oil. It's an easy process to make your own garlic oil (see Index). It won't be as strong as the capsules but are an advantage for children, they cannot tolerate full-strength garlic oil.

EYEBATHS

There are a few very important things to know about eyebaths:

• Everything you use when dealing with eyes must be scrupulously clean and dust-free.

• Made-up eyewash should not be kept for more than 2 days and must be stored in the refrigerator in a sterilised, well-covered jar.

• If both eyes are infected you should use separate eyebaths or sterilise the eyebaths before treating the second eye, to prevent cross-infection from one to the other.

You can buy special eyecups or eyebaths from a pharmacy. Buy more than one. Immerse them in boiling water before and after use. To use the eyebath, fill it three-quarters full of warm infusion or decoction which has been filtered through coffee filter paper.

(If there is a lot of inflammation or swelling, the liquid may be used cold.) Hold the eyebath firmly over the eye, tilt the head back and blink rapidly several times.

Use the treatment 2–6 times a day depending on the severity of the problem.

FOOT BATHS

As the name suggests, this is a bath for the feet but an ideal vessel would be deep enough to cover the calves of the legs as well. Most people have heard of the mustard bath but other herbs may also be used. Cold foot baths will soothe tired feet and help to stop nosebleeds.

Making a Herbal Foot Bath

2 cups (500ml/16fl oz) boiling water
3 tablespoons fresh or
1¹/₂ tablespoons dried herbs

Pour water over herbs and cover. Leave to stand 15 minutes. Strain the herbal liquid into the foot bath, add comfortably warm water and soak the feet for 10–15 minutes.

Mustard Baths

Dissolve 2 tablespoons mustard and add to a foot bath of hot water. Keep your feet immersed for 15–30 minutes, topping up with more hot water as needed.

GARGLES

Gargles are preparations for healing and soothing infected or sore throats. They can be made either from tinctures added to boiled water, or from a strong infusion or decoction. It's a good idea to have suitable dried herbs or tinctures mixed, labelled and stored in your medicine box.

INHALATIONS

To make an inhalation you need finely chopped herbs, essential oils or menthol crystals, a heat-proof bowl, boiling water and 2 large towels.

Put the bowl on a folded towel on a table; make sure it is very stable and won't slip. Half-fill the bowl with boiling water, sit in a chair, close to the table and bowl, with the towel draped over your shoulders.

Put a good handful of finely chopped herbs on the surface of the water or sprinkle with a few menthol crystals or about ten drops of your chosen oil. (You can use a mixture of herbs and oils if you like.) Immediately cover your head, shoulders and the bowl and lean over the steam for 10 minutes. If the mixture seems to be getting weak, you can add more herbs or oil.

Don't go out of doors for some time after having an inhalation as your mucous membranes will be sensitive and cold air could have an adverse effect.

Caution:
If you are giving an inhalation to a very young or very old person you must be very careful to avoid accidents with the boiling water. Stay with the patient the whole time and hold the bowl firmly. If the patient is a baby it's better to fill the hand basin in the bathroom with boiling water, shut the door and window and sit with the baby on your knee while he or she inhales the steam filling the room from the basin. This is also a good system to use for a frail, very sick or aged person.

OINTMENTS

Making ointments is one of my greatest pleasures. Collecting the herbs from an early morning garden and transforming them into a wonderful healing cream always feels like magic and, indeed, these home-made salves do seem to work in a special way. Friends have taken my healing cream all over the world as their panacea for all things external and I hear wonderful stories about cures to dogs, cats and even chickens. Very satisfying, even if a little unexpected!

The ointment recipe given here will fill a 100g (3½oz) jar. However, it's much easier to make larger quantities which may be given as gifts. The tincture of benzoin is used for its healing and preservative properties and other tinctures can be chosen for the effect you want.

The first step is to make a quantity of Basic Herb Oil which can be used in massage oils, facial preparations, baths and ointments.

Some people like to use lanolin in these preparations but you may prefer petroleum jelly. Lanolin can sometimes be polluted by chemicals used on the wool of the sheep, not all of which can be removed during processing. Either will do and you may choose according to what you have available.

To Make Ointment

½ cube (7g/¼oz) beeswax
40g (1⅓oz) petroleum jelly or lanolin
2½ tablespoons Basic Herb Oil
2 teaspoons herb tincture
½ teaspoon tincture of benzoin

Melt beeswax gently in a small pan, then add petroleum jelly or lanoline and melt together. Add oil slowly, keeping mixture liquid, then take the pan off the heat and cool slightly. Add both tinctures, stirring until no drops of tincture can be seen in the mixture and the ointment has begun to thicken very slightly. Pot immediately.

POULTICES, FOMENTATIONS AND COMPRESSES

These methods are ways of applying heat, cold, stimulation, moisture or the healing properties of various agents to areas of the body. They can be used to draw pus or foreign bodies from flesh and are a fine treatment for relieving congestion. As a general rule, a cold compress is used for such purposes as withdrawing heat from an area or for soothing abrasions. Hot fomentations and poultices ease pain, relax spasms, draw pus and relieve congestion. They are very simple to use.

Caution:
The number one rule when using a hot fomentation or poultice is not to burn your patient. Test the temperature on your wrist before putting it on the person you are treating. Remember also that a sore, bruised or grazed area will be less able to tolerate heat than undamaged flesh and skin.

POULTICES

A poultice is made with mashed or blended herbs, hot fluid, and sometimes tinctures. It is applied as a pack to the skin and used to draw pus or foreign bodies from a wound. It can also relieve chest congestion.

To Make a Poultice

Mash or blend fresh or dried herbs into a paste with a little boiling water, infusion or decoction. A few drops of tincture may be added for extra strength. Adding bread to this mixture helps it to stay hot longer and gives it a good consistency.

Put the mixture into a cheesecloth or muslin bag, flatten it out and check its heat on the inside of your wrist. Place on the affected part, being very careful not to burn your patient. (Ask if it feels too hot.) Cover with plastic wrap and a towel or thick cloth to keep in the heat.

The poultice may be reheated between two plates over a pan of boiling water if it cools down too much. You need not make it afresh each time as long as it is still clean. Change it often for the first two hours or until some improvement is seen.

POWDERED HERBS

To make powdered herbs you need either a mortar and pestle or a coffee grinder. Grind the herbs finely enough to pass through a very fine mesh sieve and store them in a jar marked with the name of the mixture, for example haemorrhoid mixture or wound mixture. Include a list of the herbs in the mixture and the expiry date (see Drying Herbs – Storage). The grinding and sieving need to be very well done, to avoid irritation to the affected parts. I store these herbs in my refrigerator for maximum protection of their properties, as finely ground herbs and spices lose their quality far more quickly than coarse material.

FOMENTATIONS

Fomentations have similar uses to poultices but are not as powerful. They may be used where a condition is not so severe or where it would be too uncomfortable to use a poultice.

To Make a Fomentation

Soak a piece of soft cloth in a hot infusion or decoction, made at about three times normal strength. Wring out the excess liquid, test on your wrist for temperature and apply as hot as is comfortable. Cover with plastic wrap and a towel. Repeat often in the first two hours or until some relief is obtained.

COMPRESSES

Compresses are made in the same way as fomentations but cold liquid is used instead of hot. They need to be changed as soon as they become warm. Compresses are used to reduce inflammation and ease the pain of sprains.

POULTICES, FOMENTATIONS AND COMPRESSES

ABSCESSES

REMEDY:
Garlic, hyssop, marjoram, oregano, sage, yarrow

HOW TO USE:
As many of the herbs as possible used as fomentation or poultice. Repeat 3 hourly.

ARTHRITIS

REMEDY:
Cider vinegar, mullein, thyme

HOW TO USE:
Fomentation. Twice daily.

BOILS

REMEDY: Comfrey leaf and root, ginger root, plantain

HOW TO USE: Pound some or all of the herbs together with oats, bran or bread and boiling water to form a paste. Apply as a poultice. Renew every 3 hours.

BRUISES AND BLACK EYES

REMEDY:
a) Chamomile, witch hazel, yarrow
b) Hyssop, marjoram or oregano

HOW TO USE:
a) Cold compress
b) Mash together to form a cold paste. Apply to the bruised area. Renew as soon as warm.

CYSTS

REMEDY:
Cayenne*, mullein, plantain, cider vinegar

HOW TO USE:
Poultice or fomentation. Repeat 3 times daily
*Use 1 part cayenne to 8 parts other herbs.

CYSTITIS

REMEDY:
Cayenne*, chamomile, plantain, wormwood, yellow dock

HOW TO USE:
Hot fomentation over the bladder using as many of the herbs as possible. Repeat 2 hourly until relief is obtained.
*Use 1 part cayenne to 8 parts other herbs.

GLANDS, SWOLLEN

REMEDY:
Mullein, plantain, yarrow, yellow dock

HOW TO USE:
Hot fomentation every 2 hours using as many of the herbs as possible.

INFLAMMATION

REMEDY:
Calendula, hyssop, mallow, marjoram, oregano, mullein, tansy. Witch hazel extract

HOW TO USE:
Very cold compress using at least 4 of the herbs. Sprinkle witch hazel onto the compress before applying. Reapply when the compress is warm.

NEURALGIA

REMEDY:
Cayenne*, chamomile, mullein, wormwood

HOW TO USE:
Apply a hot fomentation. Repeat every hour until relief is obtained.
*Use 1 part cayenne to 8 parts other herbs.

NIPPLES, SORE

REMEDY:
Calendula, mallow, yarrow

HOW TO USE:
Apply a triple strength infusion as a compress every 2 hours. Follow with calendula ointment (see page 92).

RHEUMATISM

REMEDY:
Cayenne*, cider vinegar, hyssop, mullein, thyme, wormwood

HOW TO USE:
Poultice or fomentation twice daily.
*Use 1 part cayenne to 8 parts other herbs.

SKIN, CUTS AND TEARS

REMEDY:
Calendula, comfrey leaf and root, rosemary, thyme, yarrow

HOW TO USE:
Compress using as many as possible of the herbs, use twice daily.

SORES, RUNNING

REMEDY:
Calendula, comfrey leaf and root, plantain, rosemary, sage, thyme, violet, yarrow

HOW TO USE:
Mash and pound as many as possible of the herbs with oats, bran or bread to form a paste. Apply 3 times daily to the sores as a warm poultice.

SORE THROAT

REMEDY:
Cayenne*, cider vinegar, hyssop, mullein, yarrow, yellow dock

HOW TO USE:
Make a hot fomentation with as many of the above as possible. Soak a piece of folded towelling in the liquid, wring out and wrap around the throat. Cover with a dry cloth to keep the heat in. Repeat 2 hourly.
*Use 1 part cayenne to 8 parts other herbs.

SPRAINS AND SWELLINGS

REMEDY:
Calendula, chamomile, cider vinegar, comfrey leaf and root, ginger, mallow, tansy, wormwood. Witch Hazel.

HOW TO USE:
Make a triple strength infusion of as many of the above as possible. Sprinkle witch hazel on the compress, apply as cold as possible. Renew as the compress warms up.

ULCERS

REMEDY:
Calendula, comfrey leaf and root, mallow, sage, thyme, violet

HOW TO USE:
Poultice and/or fomentation

VARICOSE VEINS

REMEDY:
Calendula, plantain, witch hazel

HOW TO USE:
Very cold compress using all the above. Apply 2 or 3 times daily while the leg is elevated.

WOUNDS

REMEDY:
Calendula, comfrey leaf and root, mallow, oregano, mullein, plantain, rosemary, yarrow

HOW TO USE:
Use as many as possible of the herbs made into a poultice, fomentation or compress.

NOSE PACKS

Packing the nose can help to stop nosebleeds. There are 2 ways of doing this:
◆ Roll a small piece of cotton wool into a cylinder and soak it in the tincture or juice of plantain or shepherd's purse. Gently insert it into the nose and leave for as long as possible. Be very careful when removing it to avoid restarting the bleeding.
◆ Bruise the leaf of plantain or shepherd's purse until it becomes juicy, roll it into a cylinder and push it very gently into the nose. Remove carefully to avoid starting the bleeding again.

Keep the patient's hands above their head or soak the hands or feet in a bowl of very cold water. Either of these treatments will help.

SUPPOSITORIES

This is a mixture with healing agents in a base with a low melting point. It is used in the rectum, vagina or nostrils. My favourite base is cocoa butter. This is available through pharmacies or direct from pharmaceutical suppliers. Cocoa butter is the fat extract from the crushed, roasted seeds of the cocoa plant (*Theobroma cacao*).

Cocoa butter is useful in both medicinal and skin-care preparations. It is a fine emollient with a very low melting point, so it liquefies easily on contact with the skin. The other thing in its favour is that it smells really good. Never put cocoa butter in a pan directly on the heat source. Its melting point is so low that it burns very easily. Melt it in a bowl over a pan of hot water or a double boiler.

To Make Suppositories

Melt 60g (2oz) cocoa butter as described above. Mix in finely powdered dried herbs until the mixture is the consistency of very thick gravy. You can add 5–10 drops of tincture to strengthen the effect of the preparation. If you want to use more tincture, you may need to add a little melted beeswax to get a better 'set'.

Take the pan off the heat and stir until the mixture is of a moulding consistency. Rectal suppositories should be about 5cm (2in) long, about as thick as the middle finger and slightly conical. Adapt the thickness to your own requirements. Vaginal suppositories (also known as pessaries) are shorter and more conical. Use sanitary pads to protect underwear.

WOUND WASHES

A dirty injury needs to be washed clean before any further treatment takes place. The water used to wash the wound should, ideally, be sterile, which means boiling it for ten minutes, then allowing it to cool, covered. Add any of the following to the sterilised water:
• Powdered vulnerary and/or antiseptic herbs, made into an infusion and strained.
• A few drops of suitable essential oil.
• Tinctures: 10 drops of tincture to every 1 cup (250ml/8fl oz) of water.

If the injury is to a foot or hand, the part can be immersed in a bowl. If it is a limb which is wounded, use cotton wool as a gentle swab.

Garlic Oil

250g (8oz) garlic cloves
olive oil

Peel and chop the garlic finely. Put in a jar and cover completely with warm olive oil. Leave in a warm place for one week. Strain through 4 layers of fine cheesecloth or muslin. Bottle in amber glass and store in a cool dark place.

Horseradish Vinegar

Finely grate fresh horseradish root and cover with cider vinegar. Stand for 2 weeks, then strain.

GLOSSARY OF MEDICAL TERMS

ALTERATIVE
A substance which changes a bodily function

ANTI-INFLAMMATORY
Reduces inflammation in tissues

ANTISEPTIC
An agent which prevents sepsis

ANTISPASMODIC
Prevents or eases spasms

APERIENT
An opening, laxative agent

AROMATIC
Adds pleasant taste and odour to medicines

ASTRINGENT
Causes contraction of soft tissue

CARMINATIVE
Expels wind and eases griping pains

DEMULCENT
Softens and lubricates internally

DIAPHORETIC
Promotes perspiration

DIGESTIVE
Aids digestion

DIURETIC
Increases elimination of urine from body

EMOLLIENT
Softens and smooths the skin

EXPECTORANT
Helps to expel mucus

HAEMOSTATIC
Having the power to stop bleeding

HEPATIC
Aids the working of the liver

NERVINE
Strengthens and calms the nerves

RELAXANT
Helps to produce an overall calming and relaxing effect

STIMULANT
Energy producing

TONIC
Aids in strengthening an organ oor whole body

WOUND HEALING
Aids the healing of wounds and inflammations

MEDICINAL PROPERTIES

This list will give you some insight into the functional effects of the many constituents in each herb.

ALTERATIVE
Echinacea, nettle, plantain, red clover, violet, yarrow, yellow dock

ANTI-INFLAMMATORY
Calendula, chamomiles, comfrey, dandelion, liquorice, sage, thyme, violet

ANTISEPTIC
Anise, calendula, garlic, nasturtium, shepherd's purse

ANTISPASMODIC
Angelica, basil, catnep, chamomiles, coriander, dill, lavender, lemon balm, peppermint, spearmint, mullein, oregano, rosemary, rue, thyme, valerian

APERIENT
Dandelion, yellow dock

AROMATIC
Aniseed, angelica, coriander, fennel, ginger, lemon balm, liquorice, peppermint, spearmint

ASTRINGENT
Comfrey, nettle, plantain, sage, yellow dock

CARMINATIVE
Anise, bergamot, caraway, catnep, coriander, dill, ginger, peppermint, spearmint

DEMULCENT
Borage, chickweed, liquorice, mallow, mullein

DIAPHORETIC
Cayenne, elder, ginger, hyssop, lemon balm, peppermint, rosemary, spearmint

DIGESTIVE
Angelica, ginger, peppermint, parsley, thyme, yarrow

DIURETIC
Angelica, dandelion, parsley, tarragon, watercress

EMOLLIENT
Borage, comfrey, liquorice, mallow, mullein

EXPECTORANT
Angelica, anise, caraway, ginger, horseradish, hyssop, liquorice, mullein, thyme

HAEMOSTATIC
Calendula, plantain, sage, shepherd's purse, yarrow .

HEPATIC
Dandelion, sage

NERVINE
Lavender, rosemary, valerian

RELAXANT
Catnep, chamomile, lavender, rosemary, valerian

STIMULANT
Cayenne, feverfew, ginger, hyssop

TONIC
Alfalfa, peppermint, spearmint, oregano, rue, savories, wormwood

WOUND-HEALING
Aloe, calendula, chamomile, comfrey, elder, feverfew, lavender, mallow, nettle, plantain, rosemary, sage, shepherd's purse, thyme, valerian, violet, yarrow

USING HERBS FOR HEALING

There are several ways to use your chosen herbs. The easiest is called a 'simple', meaning that only one herb is used. For instance, a cup of chamomile tea at bedtime can help you achieve a good night's sleep or ginger tea can settle a queasy stomach. If you want to use simples, Herb Know How, at the beginning of this book, can help you to identify suitable herbs for different purposes.

The more usual and possibly safer way to use the herbs is as a 'compound', using several herbs in a mixture. The reasons for this are:

1. Some problems need a variety of actions for relief to be gained, as a disorder in one organ can result in other organs becoming involved and needing treatment. For instance, a sluggish liver would require the use of hepatic and possibly digestive, antispasmodic and aperient herbs. A herb used in such a way to address a problem directly is known as an 'active botanical'.

2. Where there is inflammation or irritation present it is necessary to use certain herbs to buffer the action of the other ingredients and to soothe membranes.

3. Some herbal mixtures taste terrible and the use of aromatics helps to make them more acceptable.

4. An aperient, unless diarrhoea is a problem, is always helpful; having the bowels functioning well helps the system rid itself of toxins.

A formula for a herbal compound, therefore could be:
- 3 parts active botanical (see 1 at left)
- 1 part demulcent (see 2 at left)
- 1 part aromatic (see 3 at left)
- 1 part aperient, unless diarrhoea is present (see 4 above)

A typical formula for arthritis could be:
- 1 part nettle: diuretic, alternative, alkalising and calcium-rich
- 1 part dandelion: diuretic, laxative, tonic
- 1 part elderflower: anti-inflammatory, alterative, diaphoretic

Help

Help is sometimes needed to make changes in areas which have been unbalanced for a long time, but these days we are fortunate that there are professional therapists who use many techniques to help us release our tensions. Some therapists use specialised massage to release muscular tension patterns and the underlying emotional causes. Others use breath therapy to allow us to reach those hidden angers and griefs which can distort our lives. There are many ways these days to 'get in touch' with the various vulnerable inner aspects of ourselves. Newsagents, local government offices and health centres can often advise you of therapists who could be of help to you.

HEALTHY REMEDIES

ABRASIONS

REMEDY:
Calendula, mallow, plantain, yarrow

HOW TO USE:
Wash with an Infusion of the above herbs. Apply an Ointment made from the above herbs. Cover with a dressing if necessary.

ALLERGIES

REMEDY:
a) Dandelion, elderflower, red clover, violet leaves
b) Vitamin C, garlic capsules, tincture of echinacea

HOW TO USE:
a) Eat in salads once daily. Make as a tea blend and drink one cup 3 times daily.
b) Take 2g vitamin C and 3 garlic capsules daily plus 10 drops of tincture of echinacea in 1 tablespoon water once a day, 6 days a week for up to 1 year to strengthen the autoimmune system.

ANAEMIA

REMEDY:
Alfalfa, dandelion leaf, watercress and landcress, paprika, parsley, red clover, garlic

HOW TO USE:
Eat salads containing the above vitamin C and iron-rich herbs twice a day or as often as possible.

APPETITE DEPRESSANT

REMEDY:
Fennel, anise and caraway seeds

HOW TO USE:
Chew a few seeds when hungry to depress appetite.

ARTHRITIS

The general term 'arthritis' indicates inflammation of a joint. Osteoarthritis, rheumatoid arthritis, and gout are some of the conditions which fall into this category. Herbal remedies aim at the cleansing of acid waste and congestion in the tissues; improving the circulation in the affected area by the use of massage oils; building up the autoimmune system. Reduction of the intake of animal and refined foods is also an important factor. See also Essential Oils Chart for massage oils.

REMEDY:
a) Dandelion leaves and ground roast root
b) Nettle, parsley, peppermint
c) Echinacea

HOW TO USE:
a) Eat the dandelion leaves in salads and sandwiches. Use the ground roast root as a coffee-like drink.
b) Make the herbs into a tincture and take 15 drops in 2 tablespoons water 3 times daily before meals.
c) 10 drops echinacea tincture a day, 6 days of the week, for up to 1 year.

ASTHMA

During an attack of asthma the tubes responsible for carrying air in and out of the lungs spasm and become narrower. It then becomes difficult for the patient to breathe and this in turn often creates panic which can make the situation worse. An attack is often triggered by chest infections and the secretion of thick and sticky mucus which also contributes to the shortness of breath.

An attempt should be made to prevent rather than treat asthma attacks, as serious attacks require prompt professional attention. All or some of the following suggestions may help: breathing exercises; reducing anxiety and stress; avoiding irritants and allergens such as house-dust mite, very cold air, emotional stress, tobacco smoke and factory or vehicle air pollution; seeking dietary advice to eliminate potential food allergens from the diet.

The following herbs may be useful for their ability to cleanse mucus from the lungs. See also

Essential Oils chart. Use as a preventive if there are signs of a cough or mucus build-up.

REMEDY:
Expectorants; red clover, liquorice, elderflower, hyssop, thyme, violet
Relaxants; chamomile, catnep

HOW TO USE:
Infusion using 3 parts expectorant herbs (a mixture of as many of the above herbs as possible), 1 part either of the relaxant herbs. Adults 1 cup 3 times daily for 6 days. Children see Dosage, page 88.

BITES AND STINGS

See FIRST AID CHART

BLEEDING, EXTERNAL AND INTERNAL

See FIRST AID CHART

BOILS AND CARBUNCLES

Boils and carbuncles are staphylococcal infections of the hair roots. Carbuncles are a collection of several boils. The infection is easily spread to surrounding areas so great cleanliness is needed during treatment.

Use tissues and cotton wool balls to clean and treat the area and destroy as soon as the treatment is completed. Clothing which comes in contact with the infected area should be washed separately from the family laundry and a few drops of eucalyptus or tea tree oil added to the final rinse.

Boils can be an indication of poor dietary intake or overeating; diabetes; kidney disease. If the problem persists, professional help needs to be sought to check the reason.

REMEDY:
a) Red clover sprouts. Tincture of echinacea. Garlic capsules and fresh cloves.
b) Calendula tincture. Calendula and mallow ointment.

HOW TO USE:
a) Eat fresh red clover sprouts twice daily. Take 15 drops tincture in 1 tablespoon water 3 times daily for 3 weeks. Take 2 garlic capsules 3 times daily for 1 week. Reduce to 1 capsule 3 times daily until boils are healed.
b) Wash boil and large surrounding area of skin

(to prevent infection spreading) frequently with cottonwool balls dipped in calendula tincture diluted half and half with boiled water.

Make an ointment containing calendula, mallow herbs and tea tree oil. Apply to the boil and cover with a dressing.

BREATH, BAD

See ESSENTIAL OILS chart.

BRONCHITIS

REMEDY:
a) Angelica (leaf or root), aniseed, hyssop, mullein, thyme, violet
b) Echinacea, garlic

HOW TO USE:
a) Make an infusion of as many as possible of the herbs. Take 1 cup 3 times daily. Dosage for children see page 88.
b) Take 20 drops tincture of echinacea every 2 hours for 10 days. Take garlic as for boils above.

BRUISES

If you bruise easily it could be an indication of a lack of vitamin C.

REMEDY:
Calendula, comfrey leaf, plantain, yarrow, witch hazel extract

HOW TO USE:
Make a triple strength infusion of as many of the herbs as possible, allow to cool. Mix half and half with witch hazel extract. Cool in the refrigerator and apply very cold as a compress to the bruised area. Repeat every 2 hours for the first day then 3 times daily.

BURNS, MINOR (FIRST-DEGREE)

Only first-degree burns should be treated at home, all other burns require medical attention. A description of the various degrees of burns follows:

First-degree burns: Scalds and sunburn. Red and painful but skin isn't broken. May be treated at home.

Second-degree burns: Very red, blistered and painful. Cover with dry sterile dressing and get medical aid.

Third-degree burns: Not necessarily painful as nerve endings may be destroyed. Cover with dry sterile dressing and get immediate medical aid.

REMEDY:
Cold water. Tea tree oil, lavender oil, aloe gel, tincture of echinacea. Witch hazel extract.

HOW TO USE:
Run cold water over the burnt area for at least 10 minutes. If this isn't possible apply cold compresses for the same length of time, changing very often. Smooth on any of the above remedies or apply cold compresses of witch hazel extract.

CATARRH

Catarrh may be the result of a cold or influenza but may also be a sign of an intolerance of food – most commonly dairy products.

REMEDY:
a) Hyssop, thyme, mallow
b) Horseradish
c) Thyme oil
d) Garlic capsules

HOW TO USE:
a) Drink an infusion of the mixed herbs 3 times daily for 6 days. After a break of 2 days the treatment may be repeated until relief is obtained, always allowing a break of 2 days between treatments.
b) 1 teaspoon horseradish vinegar sweetened with honey in half a glass of water. Take 3 times daily.
c) Inhale with thyme oil (see Inhalations for instructions)
d) Take 1 garlic capsule 3 times daily with meals.

CHILLS AND COLDS

Stay in bed and sweat it out – don't 'soldier on' and spread your cold to other unfortunates. If you suffer from many colds you may need to look at your general health and in particular the health of your autoimmune system.

REMEDY:
a) Elderflower, peppermint and yarrow
b) Tincture of echinacea, garlic capsules, vitamin C
c) Mustard Foot bath

HOW TO USE:
a) Drink an infusion of these 3 herbs (sweetened with honey if liked) while in a hot bath. Go straight to bed, drink a further cup of hot infusion which should make you begin to sweat. Drink 3–4 cups total in 1 day. Drink copious amounts of water and/or fruit juices.
b) Take 3g vitamin C daily, 1 garlic oil capsule 3 times daily with meals and 20 drops tincture of echinacea in 1 tablespoon water 4 times daily for 1 week.

CIRCULATION, POOR

REMEDY:
Chilli, garlic, ginger, horseradish

HOW TO USE:
Use daily in food

CONSTIPATION

Constipation may be the result of:
a) Low-fibre diet, insufficient exercise, insufficient water intake, poor muscle tone.
b) A nervous excitable disposition, often being interspersed with bouts of diarrhoea.

REMEDY
a) 1 dessertspoon linseed daily sprinkled over cereal or other food. Increase fibre in diet, eat lots of fruit and vegetables. (See Chapter 6.) Drink 6 glasses of water a day.
Walk (or other exercise) for about half an hour, at least 3 times a week.
b) 1 cup twice daily of an infusion of chamomile, lemon balm and valerian. Take for 6 days, rest on the 7th. Repeat for 1 month. And also, join a meditation group.

COUGHS

REMEDY:
Angelica, anise, fennel, hyssop, mullein

HOW TO USE:
Make a Syrup or Oxymel (see page 89) using the above herbs. Take as directed in recipe.

CUTS AND WOUNDS

REMEDY:
a) Witch hazel extract
b) Calendula tincture
c) Calendula, mallow, plantain, sage thyme, violet. Tea tree oil

HOW TO USE:
a) Apply as a compress to halt bleeding.
b) 1 teaspoon in 1 cup boiled water to wash dirt from wound if necessary. Leave uncovered if possible but if too severe use c).
c) Apply ointment made with herbs and tea tree oil. Cover with a dressing.

CYSTITIS

Commonly caused by an acid/alkali imbalance in the body which creates very acid urine.
Preventive measures
Cut out refined flours and sugars. Eats lots of fresh fruit and vegetables. Substitute dandelion coffee for tea and coffee (this will encourage a more copious flow of urine). Drink at least 8 glasses of water a day. Always empty the bladder after intercourse.
REMEDY:
a) Chamomile, mallow, nettle
b) Tincture of echinacea

HOW TO USE:
a) Observe the above recommendations during an attack and also drink 6 small cups a day of an infusion made from the above herbs. This is in addition to the recommended quantity of water.
b) Take 20–30 drops every 2 hours during an attack, reduce to 20 drops twice daily for up to 2 months to prevent recurrence.

DIARRHOEA

The treatment recommended here is for an acute (as opposed to chronic) attack of diarrhoea which may or may not be accompanied by griping pains in the stomach, nausea and vomiting. If the diarrhoea and/or vomiting is prolonged, or if the patient is a baby, professional help must be sought as the complaint may be a symptom of something more serious or may cause severe dehydration.

Eat only grated apple and drink diluted fruit juices and the astringent herbal infusions described below – this will give the bowel a rest. Continue for 2 days. On the third day, if the condition has improved, eat steamed white rice with a small serving of steamed vegetables.

REMEDY:
Plantain, sage, yarrow

HOW TO USE:
Drink 3 cups of infusion made from the above herbs daily.

EARACHE

see FIRST AID chart.

ECZEMA

Eczema is an inflammatory condition of the skin which can be difficult to treat until the underlying causes are found and treated. It may be necessary to seek the assistance of a naturopath, homeopath or other health professional in order to determine the cause.

Internally emphasis needs to be on liver cleansing (see a) below

Externally the itching may be eased with the following oil b).

REMEDY:
a) Roast, ground dandelion root
b) Calendula, chickweed, mallow
c) Tincture of echinacea

HOW TO USE:
a) Drink 3 cups daily of dandelion coffee instead of tea or coffee.
b) Make a Basic Herb Oil using mallow, chickweed and calendula. Smooth on the itchy rash as often as liked. Bathe the affected area with a triple strength infusion of chickweed.
c) take 20 drops 3 times daily for 6 days of the week for 2 months.

EYES, INFLAMED

REMEDY:
Calendula, fennel

HOW TO USE:
Make an infusion of the above herbs. Strain through coffee filter paper. Use to bathe eyes (see page 90). Store in the refrigerator in a tightly covered bottle or jar. Use within 2 days.

FEVER

See CHILLS AND COLDS

FRACTURES

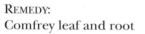

Initially a fracture needs urgent medical attention but the healing process can be accelerated by the use of herbal remedies.

REMEDY:
Comfrey leaf and root

HOW TO USE:
Poultice and ointment if the area isn't enclosed in plaster.

GALL BLADDER

The health and correct functioning of the gall bladder can be helped by drinking dandelion coffee and eating red clover sprouts.
If inflammation of the gall bladder is suspected, a course of echinacea tincture may prove helpful. Take 40 drops every 2 hours for 10 days then 20 drops 3 times a day for 1 week.

GINGIVITIS

See PYORRHOEA.

GOUT

Caused by an accumulation of uric acid in the tissues. Attention to diet is the first line of attack. Eliminate red meat, cheese, rich food and alcohol.

REMEDY:
Celery seed tincture. Dandelion root coffee.

HOW TO USE:
Take the celery tincture (available from health food stores) as recommended on the package. Drink the coffee 3 times a day as a substitute for tea or coffee.

HAEMORRHOIDS

REMEDY:
a) Calendula, nettle, plantain, shepherd's purse, yarrow
b) Witch hazel extract

HOW TO USE:
a) Insert suppositories (see page 96) made from as many as possible of the above herbs.
b) Use ice-cold compresses of witch hazel extract.

HAY FEVER

Commonly assumed to be an allergic reaction to pollen, dust, food or a number of other allergens but may be caused by a sluggish and poorly functioning liver and digestive system. The treatment can be complex and lengthy and usually needs the assistance of a health professional. The following suggestions may be tried as a preliminary treatment – they have been effective in many cases.

REMEDY:
a) Dandelion, burdock, elderflower
b) Red clover sprouts
c) Echinacea tincture

HOW TO USE:
a) Infusion or tincture of the herbs.
b) Eat raw at least twice a day.
c) 10 drops in 1 tablespoon water once a day, 6 days a week for up to 1 year.

HEARTBURN

If this is a constant problem it may be a symptom of hiatus hernia. Seek the help of a professional. If the problem is only an occasional one it may be overacidity following the eating of rich food.

REMEDY:
a) Marjoram, thyme
b) Slippery elm

HOW TO USE:
a) Use the herbs every day in cooking.
b) Take before and after meals.

HEADACHES

Headaches can arise from many causes. Some of these are stress and anxiety; illness and fever;

excessive use of alcohol; spinal misalignment; digestive disturbance. The most common headaches seem to be those caused by stress and this is the type dealt with below. Stress needs to be dealt with before it causes serious damage – meditation or stress management classes are very helpful.

REMEDY:
a) Rosemary and lavender oil used externally
b) Chamomile

HOW TO USE:
a) Massage either of the oils on the temples (avoid the eyes), the forehead and the back of the neck.
b) Sip a cup of chamomile infusion.

INDIGESTION

See HEARTBURN

INFLUENZA

Influenza is a potentially dangerous disease which is often confused with the common cold. I often hear people saying 'I've got the flu'; they are walking around, going to work and functioning fairly normally apart from feeling 'off colour', having a runny nose and maybe a cough. If these people had influenza they would be in bed with some or all of the following symptoms: high fever; aching limbs and joints; severe headache; nausea and vomiting.

   Complete bedrest is imperative in order to avoid complications.

Treatment
As for colds and chills above. Careful convalescence is needed to ensure complete recovery.

INSOMNIA

It's most important to try to find the reason for insomnia otherwise the treatments merely mask the basic problem. Stress is often a factor and can result in an inability to 'switch off' from the problems of the day. Meditation and stress management courses are very helpful.

REMEDY:
Chamomile, lemon balm. Valerian.

HOW TO USE:
Make your 'going to bed' routine slow and relaxed. Have a warm, not hot bath or shower. Sip a cup of chamomile and lemon balm infusion before going to bed. Some people find that a short, slow walk before bed is relaxing. Valerian can be used either as a tincture or an infusion if you have been suffering from insomnia for a long time.

MENSTRUAL

Heavy loss
REMEDY:
Shepherd's purse

HOW TO USE:
15 drops in 1 tablespoon water every 2 hours for 1–3 days.

Painful
REMEDY:
Catnep, chamomile, valerian

HOW TO USE:
1 small cup infusion twice a day for 1–3 days.

MIGRAINE

This is a loose term for an intense headache (often on one side of the head only) which is often accompanied by nausea, vomiting, visual disturbances and other distressing symptoms. The possibility of food allergies should be carefully investigated.
Naturopathic or homeopathic help is indicated but the following remedies have given relief to many sufferers.

REMEDY:
a) Catnep, chamomile, valerian
b) Dandelion, hyssop, wormwood, yellow dock
c) Vitamin B complex tablets
d) Feverfew

HOW TO USE:
a) Mix the above herbs or tinctures and take, before food, as a tincture – 15 drops in 1 tablespoon water twice daily or as an infusion – 1 cup twice daily. Continue for 2 months taking for 6 days only of each week.
b) Take the blended herbs as a tincture or infusion. Follow instructions for a) above.
c) Take vitamin B complex as directed on the packet.
d) Feverfew taken as tablets, tincture or infusion for a period of a month or so has cleared migraine in many, many people. A fresh leaf may be chewed but it is exceptionally bitter and causes a sore mouth in some people.

NAUSEA

REMEDY:
Peppermint

HOW TO USE:
Sip an infusion which may be sweetened with honey if liked.

NERVES, STRESSED

Once again the remedy lies with finding ways of lessening the stress rather than taking remedies to mask the symptoms. However, there are herbs which will help to lessen the stress and sleeplessness while you are dealing with the underlying causes.
If 3 doses a day of the following remedies make you feel lethargic, take at lunch and dinner time only.

REMEDY:
Catnep, chamomile, valerian

HOW TO USE:
15 drops of blended tincture in 1 tablespoon 2–3 times a day or drink 1 small cupful 2–3 times daily.

NOSEBLEEDS

REMEDY:
Plantain, shepherd's purse, witch hazel extract

HOW TO USE:
Pour some cold tincture of any of the above onto a piece of cotton wool shaped into a plug. Insert into the nostril. Pinch the nose firmly but gently with thumb and first finger above the point where the cartilage begins. Keep the patient sitting upright and maintain the pinching for at least 10 minutes. Leave the plug in place for as long as possible and take care to withdraw it very gently or the bleeding may start again.

PSORIASIS

It has been my experience that many sufferers from psoriasis have an intense craving for sugary foods. I have seen an otherwise non-greedy person eat, in one sitting, a large tub of ice cream or a large can of fruit in heavy syrup. It seems that the craving and the problem are related and sufferers from this distressing complaint would be advised to look at their food intake to see if they

are either causing or exacerbating the condition. The following recommendations for liver cleansing herbs will help to rid the body of acidity and toxicity.

REMEDY:
a) Dandelion root, rosemary, yellow dock
b) Alfalfa sprouts, red clover sprouts, young dandelion leaves
c) Vitamins A, B complex, C
d) Tincture of echinacea

HOW TO USE:
a) 15 drops tincture blend in 1 tablespoon water 3 times daily with meals. Use roast ground dandelion root as coffee instead of tea or coffee.
b) Eat as salads twice a day.
c) Take as recommended on the package.
d) Dab tincture onto affected area and take 10 drops in 1 tablespoon water once a day, 6 days a week for up to 1 year.

PYORRHOEA AND GINGIVITIS

REMEDY:
Calendula, sage, thyme

HOW TO USE:
Mouthwash 3 times daily.

RASHES

See ESSENTIAL OILS CHART

RHEUMATISM

See ARTHRITIS

RINGWORM

See also ESSENTIAL OILS CHART

REMEDY:
Calendula, myrrh

HOW TO USE:
Dab the affected area frequently with a blend of both tinctures.

SCABIES

See ESSENTIAL OILS CHART

SCALDS

See BURNS, MINOR

SHOCK

See also ESSENTIAL OILS chart

REMEDY:
Catnep, chamomile, valerian, chilli powder

HOW TO USE:
Sip a hot infusion of catnep, chamomile and valerian sweetened with honey with a tiny pinch of chilli powder stirred in.

SINUSITIS

REMEDY:
Use remedies and suggestions for Catarrh (see Essential Oils chart) and also vitamins C and A as directed on the packet.

SORES

REMEDY:
Calendula, comfrey, mallow, mullein, plantain, rosemary, thyme, violet

HOW TO USE:
Use an ointment made from as many as possible of the above herbs.

SUNBURN

See also ESSENTIAL OILS chart

REMEDY:
a) Aloe leaf
b) Lavender or witch hazel extract

HOW TO USE:
a) Spread aloe leaf gel over the burnt area, allow to dry.
b) Make a triple strength infusion from tea leaves and lavender flowers, cool and apply as compresses to the burnt area. Use witch hazel extract in the same way.

SWELLING, TISSUES

REMEDY:
Chamomile, comfrey, plantain. witch hazel extract

HOW TO USE:
Use ice-cold compresses of infusions of any or all the above herbs or an ice-cold compress of witch hazel extract.

TOOTHACHE

See ESSENTIAL OILS chart

THROAT, SORE

REMEDY:
a) Elderflower, sage, thyme
b) Tincture of echinacea

HOW TO USE:
a) Make a triple strength infusion of the herbs. Use as gargle every 2 hours until relief is obtained.
b) Add 40 drops to 1 tablespoon water. Gargle every 4 hours for 3 days. Swallow the gargle.

THRUSH

It's no good going to the trouble of treating yourself unless your partner uses the myrrh also as thrush can be sexually transmitted.

REMEDY:
a) Tincture of myrrh. Yoghurt
b) Garlic capsules, Vitamin B complex and yoghurt
c) Tincture of echinacea

HOW TO USE:
a) Add 1 teaspoon tincture to 1 cup water. Pour into the vagina while sitting on the toilet and leaning back. Bathe the penis in a small bowlful of the tincture mixture. Repeat 3 times a day until clear. Dip a tampon into yoghurt and insert into the vagina.
b) Take garlic and vitamins as recommended on the packet. Eat 1 cup live yoghurt 3 times a day.
c) During an attack, take 40 drops every 2 hours for 4 days. To increase protection take 10 drops once a day for 6 days of a week for 6 months.

VOMITING

REMEDY:
Ground ginger root, peppermint, raspberry

HOW TO USE:
Sip 1 cup of an infusion made from 1 or all of the above herbs. It may be sweetened with honey.

WARTS

REMEDY:
Dandelion juice

HOW TO USE:
Smear the juice from the broken stalk onto the wart. Avoid getting the juice on the surrounding skin. Cover and repeat often.

LIFESTYLE AND HEALTH

Physical problems can be created by many things and it's important to search for the cause before starting home treatment. For example, a headache can be the result of faulty eyesight, tight shoes, spinal problems, acidosis, anaemia, upset stomach, bad teeth, onset of influenza or a cold, hepatitis and, in 80% of cases, stress. Diarrhoea can be a symptom of gastroenteritis, worms, giardiasis, dysentery, amoebiasis and, again, stress.

If a problem is severe or of long duration, you should seek the help of a qualified professional. After establishing the nature of the problem it would then be in order to say that you would like to use herbs as part of your healing process.

Many people who are ignorant of the properties of herbs consider them to be harmless.

This is a dangerous misconception. To be of use, any herb needs pharmacological activity, this is the property which can alter the state of the body and which if used correctly can promote healing.

Conversely, if used for extended periods or in excessive doses, it can cause problems. I have said elsewhere in this book that dose recommendations must be adhered to and that no medicines should be taken for more than 6 days of the week, the seventh day being a rest for the system. It's good to eat very simply on this day, soups, salads or juices and to have pleasant exercise and relaxation.

If you suffer with acid stomach, bowel cramps, pain in the neck or any other ongoing complaints, it is good to sit quietly with a piece of paper and a pencil and make lists for every aspect of your life – parenthood, spirituality, sex, recreation, finances, friends and/or workmates and any other area which you may feel is relevant. Give each a mark out of 10, 10 being the best and 1 the worst. If an aspect scores 5 or less, your life is out of balance and your health will be unbalanced.

At some time or other we have all used such expressions as 'you're a pain in the neck' or 'you make me sick', and this can actually happen. In conflict situations the muscles become so tense that they can't relax, and excess adrenalin causes complex situations in the body which, if not resolved, may lead to physical as well as emotional problems.

CHILDREN

When treating children we need to be very careful to use only the most gentle remedies. The herbs suggested here have all been shown over centuries to be suitable for children but, even so, we must never forget that everything on this planet will be an allergen to someone. If your child suffers from allergies, be aware that chamomile, for instance, could cause a problem. A 'patch' test can be helpful for both children and adults. To do this, make a very strong infusion of the suspected herb, dab it thoroughly on the inside skin of the elbow, cover and leave for 24 hours. If there is any redness or soreness at the end of this time the herb should be avoided.

It's good to encourage children to drink mild herbal teas, mixed with fresh fruit juices, from an early age. If they develop a taste for these drinks it will have twofold benefits: drinking the teas is a preventive act, and the children won't be resistant to the teas if they are sick. Herbs which are good to use for these drinks are lemon grass, spearmint and red raspberry leaf or fruit, mixed with apple, orange or lemon juice, water and honey. Fruit juices should always be diluted with water or herb tea before being given to children; the undiluted juice is too strong for small, immature digestive systems to cope with. Avoid giving the same herb over long periods. Vary them from day to day.

RECIPES FOR BABIES

Colic

For convenience make powdered mixtures, store them in glass jars and mark with the mixture name. You might find that one blend is more effective for your baby than another. If the problem persists, seek professional help.

Colic Mixture 1

Anise seed
Fennel seed
Dill seed

Colic Mixture 2

Catnep, dried
Spearmint, dried
Dill seed

Colic Mixture 3

Chamomile, dried
Lemon grass, dried
Fennel seed

Make all the Colic Mixtures into an infusion (see Infusion or Tea). Give in doses of 1–2 teaspoons as needed.

Cradle Cap

Chamomile flowers
Elderflower flowers
Calendula petals
Nettle, dried
Almond oil

Make a Basic Herb Oil using the herbs and massage gently into the scalp. This is a lovely oil to use all over your baby's body.

Nappy Rash

Make an ointment (see recipe in Ointments, page 92). Use chamomile, elderflower, lemon grass and mallow root to make the Basic Herb Oil and substitute cod liver oil for 10ml (2 teaspoons) of the Basic Herb Oil in the recipe. This recipe makes a really effective, soothing and healing ointment which acts as a barrier cream as well. The ointment may stain, so use a nappy liner.

Babies should be allowed to crawl around with their bare bottoms exposed to the fresh air for some part of every day as a good preventive measure. Be sure to keep them out of the sun at the hottest part of a summer's day though, to protect their skin. Small babies love being in a pram under a tree, no nappy, legs waving in the air, watching the leaves and the clouds moving. It keeps them, and you, happy for hours. A strong net (cat- and insect-proof) fastened firmly over the pram is a safety precaution.

MOUTH ULCERS

REMEDY:
Mallow, sage, thyme

HOW TO USE:
Make a Mouthwash (see Care of Your Mouth) using the herbs. Use as directed or freeze and suck a cube when the problem arises. Frequent outbreaks of mouth ulcers would suggest a vitamin/mineral deficiency or other problem. Seek professional advice.

NAPPY RASH

REMEDY:
Calendula, chamomile, elder-flower, lemon grass

HOW TO USE:
Use ointment (see Ointments) made from these herbs.

NOSEBLEED

REMEDY:
Mullein, plantain, yarrow

HOW TO USE:
Pack the nose with a cotton wool plug soaked in a cold triple strength infusion. Pinch the nose firmly but gently with the thumb and first finger above the point where the cartilage begins. Keep the patient sitting upright and maintain the pinching for at least 10 minutes. Leave the plug in place for as long as possible and take care to withdraw it very gently or the bleeding may start again. Putting the hands of the patient in cold water is often very effective.

RESTLESSNESS

REMEDY:
Catnep, chamomile, hyssop

HOW TO USE:
Give an infusion sweetened with honey. See opening notes for dosage.

STOMACHACHE

Stomachache in children can be indicative of many different problems some of which are simple and easily cured such as overeating, constipation, nerves, tiredness. Others might be an indication of a serious problem such as appendicitis. If a stomachache is severe or prolonged it requires medical attention.

OVEREATING A
CONSTIPATION

REMEDY:
Spearmint, dill, ginge

HOW TO USE:
Give an infusion swee
opening notes for do

NERVES AND T

REMEDY:
Catnep, chamomile

HOW TO USE:
Give an infusion swee
opening notes for do

TEETHING

REMEDY:
a) Catnep, chamomil

b) Catnep, lemon bal

HOW TO USE:
Give infusions sweete
or b). See opening n

TONSILLITIS

REMEDY:
a) Catnep, chamomil

b) Hyssop, sage

HOW TO USE:
a) Infusion sweetened
See opening notes fo

b) Gargle (see Gargle

VOMITING

See the cautions and
above. Vomiting can
adequate fluid intake
Never give flat lemon
from vomiting as the
dehydration. Seek pro
vomiting persists.

REMEDY:
Anise, ginger, spearm

HOW TO USE:
Sip 2 teaspoons of inf
as often as needed.

CHILDREN'S HEALTH CHART

DOSAGE

Adult dose: 125ml ($^1/_2$ cup) 3 times daily, $^1/_2$ hour before food.

Children:	30kg (66lb) plus	half adult dose
	15–29kg (33–64lb)	quarter adult dose
	7–14kg (15–31lb)	eighth adult dose

Discontinue treatment with the chosen herb after 3 weeks. Resume after a further week if treatment is working or change to another herb if no improvement is seen.

BEDWETTING

REMEDY:
a) Alfalfa sprouts, red clover sprouts

b) Lemon balm, mullein, plantain

c) Honey

HOW TO USE:
a) Eat fresh twice daily.

b) Give infusion sweetened with honey 3 times daily. See opening note for dosage.

c) 1 teaspoonful before bed.

BITES

See HEALTHY REMEDIES chart

CATARRH

REMEDY:
a) Alfalfa sprouts, red clover sprouts

b) Anise, chamomile, fennel, hyssop, lemon balm, mullein

HOW TO USE:
a) Eat fresh twice daily.

b) Give infusion sweetened with honey or oxymel (see Oxymels) 3 times daily. See opening notes for dosage.

CHICKENPOX

REMEDY:
a) Catnep, red raspberry, spearmint

b) Yarrow

HOW TO USE:
a) Give infusion sweetened with honey 3 times daily. See opening notes of chart for dosage.

b) Make a double strength infusion. Dab on spots, leave to dry.

COLDS

REMEDY:
Angelica, catnep, chamomile, spearmint

HOW TO USE:
Give infusion sweetened with honey 3 times daily. Add 8 drops cider vinegar to each tablespoon liquid.

COLIC

REMEDY:
a) Anise seed, fennel seed, dill seed

b) Catnep, spearmint, dill

c) Chamomile, lemon grass, fennel seed

HOW TO USE:
Give an infusion of a), b) or c) sweetened with honey. Give 1–2 teaspoons of the mixture as needed.

CONSTIPATION

REMEDY:
Chamomile, elderflower, mallow, mullein

HOW TO USE:
Give infusion sweetened with honey 3 times daily. See opening notes for dosage.

CRADLE CAP

REMEDY:
Chamomile, elderflower, calendula petals, nettle, almond oil

HOW TO USE:
Make a Basic Herb Oil using the herbs and massage gently into the scalp. This oil may also be used on babies bottoms and all over their bodies.

COUGH

REMEDY:
Angelica, anise, hyssop, mallow, mullein, sage, thyme, violet. Cider vinegar

HOW TO USE:
Administer the herbs in an oxymel (see Oxymels). Add 2 drops cider vinegar to each teaspoon of mixture.

CUTS AND HAEMORRHAGE

REMEDY:
Calendula, mullein, plantain, yarrow

HOW TO USE:
Compress (see Compresses).

EARACHE

See also ESSENTIAL OILS chart

REMEDY:
Garlic Oil

HOW TO USE:
Pour a few drops Garlic Oil into a warm, sterile teaspoon. Draw up into an ear dropper, squeeze gently into the ear. Plug the outside of the ear with cotton wool.

Caution:
The pure oil from garlic oil capsules must never be used in the ears of children. It is far too strong and could cause intense pain and damage to the eardrum. If the earache is intense and/or prolonged, seek professional help. Earache can be an indication of severe problems.

FEVERS

REMEDY:
a) Angelica, catnep, chamomile

b) Dill, hyssop, yarrow

c) Elderflower, spearmint, yarrow

HOW TO USE:
Give an infusion of any of the above blends sweetened with honey and add 1 teaspoon lemon juice to each cup of infusion. See opening notes for dosage.

GERMAN ME[ASLES] (RUBELLA)

REMEDY:
a) Catnep, chamo[

b) Red raspberry, [

HOW TO USE:
Give infusion of ei[
honey 3 times dail[
dosage. See also C[
easing itchy skins.

GLANDS AND [

REMEDY:
a) Catnep, ginger, [

b) Cider vinegar, [

HOW TO USE:
a) Give infusion of [
times daily. See op[

b) Use as fomenta[

HEADACHE

REMEDY:
Catnep, chamomil[

HOW TO USE:
Give an infusion sw[
opening notes for [

INSOMNIA

REMEDY:
Catnep, chamomil[

HOW TO USE:
Give an infusion sw[
warm (not hot) ba[
'low key'.

MEASLES

See GERMAN MEASL[

Measles is a poten[
Professional help [

THE FIRST AID BOX

Everyone, at some time has been, or will be, faced with a major or minor injury to themselves or others: cuts, burns and stings, and more serious things such as heart attacks and broken bones. Knowing what to do in these situations can prevent excessive trauma or pain and in some instances can save a life.

It should be noted that this section deals with first aid. Many injuries need professional help as soon as possible. The dirt in a seemingly innocent cut can carry infections such as tetanus. The pain of earache may be a symptom of middle ear infection, a potentially serious condition.

There are three things needed in order to be an effective helper:

◆ Take a short first aid course with a reputable organisation such as the St John Ambulance Brigade. Buy a good reference book on first aid to keep handy. If possible, familiarise yourself with the most common procedures *before* something happens. The middle of a crisis is not a good time to have to learn a new skill.

◆ Provide the car and house with well-equipped first aid boxes. Check them regularly and re-stock as supplies run low. Ideally, the containers should be robust, weatherproof and, if you have children, lockable.

◆ Keep a list of emergency numbers (ambulance, doctor, hospital, Poisons Information Centre), both in the first aid boxes and next to the telephone.

You can make some items for your first-aid box from your home-grown herbs, while others are best to buy ready made from the health food shop or pharmacy. You may, of course wish to vary these suggestions for your first aid supplies to suit your own family needs.

ALOE VERA GEL

Buy a reputable brand of pure aloe gel and use it on minor burns and scalds.

CHARCOAL TABLETS

This antacid remedy, used as far back as the ancient Egyptians, is a powerful absorbent in the stomach and intestinal tract, acting like a sponge. Modern charcoal is 'activated', treated with steam to make it even more absorbent. It disinfects and deodorises, picks up harmful bacteria and passes them from the body. Some say it can cure a hangover. Use with care as it can cause constipation if overused, but it is useful to treat simple diarrhoea.

GARLIC OIL CAPSULES

Garlic oil contains a very powerful antibacterial agent called allicin, which prevents the growth of bacteria, and also promotes the healing of infections. This makes it an ideal preventive herb. It may be used to ease the pain of simple earache. Squeeze a garlic oil capsule into a warmed teaspoon, add $1/2$ teaspoon olive oil. Drip into the ear and plug the external ear area with cotton wool.

IPECAC (IPECACUANHA) SYRUP

This Brazilian herb, used in small doses, is an expectorant and in large doses becomes an emetic. Its main use in the first aid box is its emetic properties in cases of poisoning. It must never be used if a strong corrosive liquid or a substance with strong fumes has been swallowed or if the patient is an infant under a year old. Always follow the instructions on the manufacturer's label.

In cases of child poisoning, it is always best to obtain urgent medical advice before you administer any remedy. Your doctor, ambulance service, health service or, if you have one, Poisons Information Centre or equivalent service will usually give advice over the phone on what to take, according to what has been swallowed.

LINSEEDS

The seeds of the flax plant are brown in colour with a smooth, shiny husk. Placed under the lower eyelid, the seed swells up into a gelatinous mass and attaches itself to foreign bodies in the eye. It then moves to the corner of the eye and can be lifted out.

MENTHOL CRYSTALS

Menthol is crystallised out of peppermint oil. In the first aid box it is used as an inhalation.

OILS

Castor oil comes from the seed of the castor oil plant and was once used as a laxative, but is no longer considered a safe treatment. As an external remedy, it has amazing drawing power, soothing as it draws splinters or foreign bodies from the flesh or the eye.

Lavender oil, distilled from the flower head, acts as a sedative, and a treatment for minor burns and scalds.

Rosemary oil, distilled from the leaf, is a treatment for muscular tension.

Tea tree oil, distilled from leaves of the *Melaleuca alternifolia*, is almost a first aid kit on its own, with powerful antibacterial and antiseptic properties. Use neat on superficial cuts, abrasions and cold sores.

OINTMENTS

Make these by following the method described in Ointments.

POWDERED HERBS

Wound-healing herbs which have been dried and ground to a powder are used where a wound needs to be kept dry. For the method see the instructions for Powdered Herbs. For appropriate herbs see Cuts and Grazes in the First Aid chart.

DR BACH'S RESCUE REMEDY

This is a ready-made mixture of the homeopathic flower tinctures cherry plum, clematis, impatiens, rock rose, and star of Bethlehem. This tincture is useful in any minor or major situation where there is shock and nerves need to be calmed. It is taken 4 drops at a time onto the tongue. Use as often as every 15 minutes if the situation warrants it. It can be rubbed on the pulse points if the patient is unconscious.

SLIPPERY ELM

A North American tree from which the bark is stripped for its medicinal value, although there is now some concern that the tree is becoming endangered. Usually, the whole tree is debarked and so dies. The powdered bark is a specific treatment for soothing inflamed membranes both internally and externally.

TINCTURES

Some of the tinctures you will find useful are calendula, chamomile, cayenne, ginger and shepherd's purse.

Witch hazel extract is a must as this tincture is one of the finest and gentlest astringents there is. It is available from pharmacies.

OTHER ADDITIONS

Bandages, slings, clean cloth
Plasters, eye patch
Scissors, tweezers
Steel or enamel dish
Small funnel
Thermometer
2 or 3 eye droppers
Glass or plastic 25ml medicine measure
Cotton buds and cotton wool

FIRST AID CHART

BLEEDING, EXTERNAL

REMEDY
a) Tincture of calendula or witch hazel extract
b) Plantain ointment

HOW TO USE:
a) Apply cold compress of either remedy.
Bandage firmly if possible.
b) Apply when bleeding has lessened, cover with a dressing if necessary.

BLEEDING, INTERNAL

This remedy is only to be used until professional help is available.

REMEDY
Tincture of shepherd's purse.

HOW TO USE:
Drink 15 drops in 2 tablespoons water. Repeat every 15–30 minutes if needed.

BRUISES

REMEDY
Aloe vera gel, comfrey ointment

HOW TO USE:
Massage bruised area gently with either of above.

BURNS, MINOR

To identify, see Healthy Remedies chart.

REMEDY
a) Aloe vera gel, tea tree oil, lavender oil
b) Dr Bach's Rescue Remedy

HOW TO USE:
a) Smear any of the remedies onto the burn.
Repeat every 15–20 minutes until pain is gone.
Don't cover, leave open to the air.
b) To counteract shock, administer Dr Bach's Rescue Remedy as directed on the label.

COLD SORES

REMEDY
Tea tree oil

HOW TO USE:
Dab cold sore with oil.

CUTS AND GRAZES

The life of a child seems to be punctuated by small dramas, which often result in a bruise, cut or graze. The mixtures of herbs which follow are useful in either as a wound wash or ointment. Grind the dried herbs very finely, sieve through a fine sieve and store in an airtight glass jar. One teaspoon of this mixture may be stirred into 1 cup (250ml/8fl oz) boiling water, cooled, strained and used as a wound wash. The powder may also be used as a dry antiseptic treatment on wounds.

REMEDY
a) Calendula, mallow, plantain, yarrow
b) Calendula tincture, tea tree oil

HOW TO USE:
a) Use as a wound wash, ointment or dry antiseptic treatment.
b) Add 1 teaspoon tincture and 3 drops oil to 1 cup 250ml (8fl oz) boiled water. Use to cleanse wound. Leave wound open to air unless severe. If a dressing is needed, drip 2 drops of tea tree oil on the dressing before applying.

EARACHE

REMEDY
a) Garlic oil capsules. (For children see Children's Health Chart.)
b) Tea tree oil

HOW TO USE:
a) Squeeze the contents of a garlic oil capsule into a warm teaspoon. Add $1/2$ teaspoon of olive oil, mix and drip into the ear. Plug the external opening of the ear with cotton wool.
b) Warm 1 teaspoon olive oil, add 3 drops tea tree oil. Drip into the ear and plug the external opening with cotton wool.

EYES, GRIT OR DUST

Don't attempt first aid treatment if the foreign body, such as a metal shaving, has penetrated the eye. Cover loosely with an eye patch and seek medical assistance.

REMEDY
a) Linseeds
b) Castor oil

HOW TO USE:
a) Put 1 seed under lower eyelid. Within a half an hour or so it will appear as a jelly (containing the grit) in the corner of the eye.
b) Put 3 drops in the eye and cover with an eye patch.

FAINTING

REMEDY
Lavender oil

HOW TO USE:
Loosen tight clothing and encourage the patient to put his/her head between the knees. Massage a few drops of the oil on the pulse points of the wrist and temple. Hold the bottle under the nose of the patient so that she/he breathes directly from the bottle.

FEVER

See HEALTHY REMEDIES chart

FLATULENCE

REMEDY
a) Charcoal tablets
b) Tincture of ginger

HOW TO USE:
a) Take as directed on container.
b) Add 1 teaspoon to a glass of warm water, sweeten with honey if liked. Sip slowly.

HEADACHES

REMEDY
a) Menthol crystals
b) Lavender or rosemary oil

HOW TO USE:
a) Inhalation.
b) Massage the back of the neck and the temples (avoiding the eyes).

HEARTBURN

REMEDY
a) Charcoal tablets
b) Peppermint oil

HOW TO USE:
a) Take as directed on the packet.
b) Mix 1 drop oil in 1 teaspoon honey in a glass. Fill with warm water and sip slowly.

INSECT BITES

REMEDY
a) Castor oil, witch hazel extract
b) Tea tree or lavender oil

HOW TO USE:
a) Apply a compress of either remedy.
b) Massage a few drops directly onto the bite.

NAUSEA AND VOMITING

REMEDY
a) Tincture of ginger
b) Slippery elm tablets

HOW TO USE:
a) 1 teaspoon tincture mixed into 1 teaspoon honey in a glass, stir to blend. Fill the glass with warm water and sip slowly.
b) If the vomiting has made the stomach sore, slippery elm tablets will soothe the lining of the stomach. Take as directed on the container.

POISONING

Note: Always have the number of the nearest Poisons Information Centre next to the telephone. Don't attempt home remedies unless you know exactly what type of poison has been taken. If possible use the remedies on the way to the nearest hospital so that no time is wasted.

REMEDY
a) Ipecacuanha syrup
b) Charcoal tablets and milk

HOW TO USE:
a) and b) Use to induce vomiting. Always follow the instructions on the manufacturer's label.

Caution:
For the remedies above:
a) It must never be used if kerosene (paraffin), bleach, acid or alkaline liquids have been swallowed (i.e. if the liquids are corrosive or have strong fumes which can suffocate) or if the patient is unconscious or under the age of 1 year.
b) Use as directed on the carton as a first aid measure when corrosive liquids or liquids with strong fumes have been swallowed.

SHOCK

REMEDY
a) Dr Bach's Rescue Remedy
b) Lavender oil

HOW TO USE:
a) Put directly onto the tongue as directed on the bottle. If the patient is unconscious, rub the remedy onto the pulse points every 5–10 minutes.
b) Hold the bottle under the nose for the patient to sniff.

SPLINTERS, DEEPLY EMBEDDED

REMEDY
Castor oil

HOW TO USE:
Soak lint or gauze in castor oil. Apply as a compress. Bandage loosely in place and change 2 hourly until the splinter is drawn to the surface.

SPRAINS

REMEDY
Rosemary oil, witch hazel extract

HOW TO USE:
Thoroughly dampen a piece of absorbent cloth with witch hazel extract, sprinkle with 5 drops rosemary oil, wring out and bandage onto the sprained area. Repeat 2 hourly.

Alternatively (or as well) the oil may be mixed with 1 tablespoon vegetable oil and massaged into the sprained area.

SUNBURN

REMEDY
Lavender oil, aloe vera gel

HOW TO USE:
Lukewarm bath into which is sprinkled 10 drops lavender oil. Soak for 20–30 minutes, splashing the burnt areas with the water. Apply either remedy after the bath. If a bath is not available, pat either of the remedies onto the burnt area.

CHAPTER FOUR
THE
BODY
BEAUTIFUL

To make a bath for melancholy.

Take Mallowes, pellitory of the wall, of each three handfuls,

Camomell flowers, Mellilot, of each one handfull, Hollyhocks, two

handfuls, Isop one greate handfull,

Senerick seed one ounce,

and boil them in nine gallons of water until they come to three,

then put in a quart of new milke

and go into it bloude warme or something warmer.

"STILL-ROOM BOOK" BY MARY FAIRFAX

GLOSSARY OF COSMETIC TERMS AND INGREDIENTS

ACID/ALKALINE

Skin has an acid mantle ranging between 5.5 and 6.2. This protects the skin from invasion by bacteria. Most soaps leave the skin alkaline; the skin will readjust the balance in 1–2 hours but in order to restore the acid mantle quickly it's good to use an acidic tonic (see TONING).

AGAR AGAR

A jelly prepared from various types of seaweed. It may be used to thicken recipes and is a non-animal substitute for gelatine.

ALMOND (*PRUNUS DULCIS*)

Ground sweet almonds are used cosmetically in a variety of ways. The meal may be used as a cleansing, refining, emollient scrub and the milk (see SCRUBS) is cleansing, refining and moisturising. The oil is a useful non-drying cosmetic ingredient.

AROMATHERAPY

The treatment of mental and physical complaints through the use of volatile essential oils. The method frequently employed is massage.

ARROWROOT

A white powdered starch obtainable from the root of several plants. This powder is soothing to the skin used either as a powder or mixed to a paste or gel (see BODY POWDER).

ASTRINGENT

An agent which has the power to contract tissues.

BEESWAX

A wax, secreted by bees, used to make the cell walls of the honeycomb. It is used as an emulsifier and binder in ointments, creams and salves (see COSMETIC BASICS for treatment of this wax).

BENZOIN TINCTURE

This tincture is made from alcohol and the aromatic and resinous juice of *Styrax benzoin*, a tree from Java and Sumatra. It has antiseptic, astringent, antifungal and protective properties and can be used as an aid in preserving creams and lotions.

Note:

Your pharmacist may offer you either simple or compound tincture of benzoin. It's most important that you use only simple tincture of benzoin. The compound has additives which can be toxic and harmful if massaged on the body.

BORAX (SODIUM TETRABORATE)

A mineral found on alkaline lake shores, borax is mildly alkaline and softening. It can be used effectively in most cosmetic products but must never be used internally or on broken skin. It can be combined with beeswax to form a stable emulsion. I wouldn't recommend its use in baby products.

CASTILE

A soap made from olive oil and other ingredients. Try to find one with at least 50% olive oil. It's sometimes quite difficult to get the hard white soap but the liquid is easy to find and lovely to use. My favourite liquid soap is a mixture of coconut, olive and peppermint oils.

CASTOR OIL OR RED TURKEY OIL

Castor oil has many cosmetic and medicinal uses (see THE FIRST AID BOX – OILS). When the oil is first expressed from the plant it contains many poisonous alkaloids which have to be removed before it's sold as 'medicinal' castor oil. There is another process used which produces water-miscible oil called 'sulphonated', 'treated' or 'red turkey oil'. This treatment makes the oil very suitable for bath oils as it mixes with the water. It's quite likely you will only be able to get red turkey oil from pharmaceutical wholesale suppliers as it's now considered old-fashioned.

CETOMACROGOL

See EMULSIFYING WAX below
EMULSIFYING WAX

COCOA BUTTER (*THEOBROMA CACAO*)

A solid fat extracted from the roasted, crushed seed of the cocoa plant. This fine emollient has a very low melting point and liquefies on contact with the skin. It is used in creams, ointments and lotions where its properties help to prevent and/or soften wrinkles and stretch marks and aid in the treatment of skin rashes, and it has the added advantage of smelling deliciously of chocolate. If you have problems obtaining it from your pharmacy, I suggest you try a pharmaceutical wholesale house. They are usually quite happy to supply on a cash basis. For ease of measuring small amounts, it may be treated in the same way as beeswax (see COSMETIC BASICS).

COCONUT OIL

A white saturated fat with a very low melting point, extracted from the white meat of the coconut. Coconut oil is beneficial to the skin and hair.

DEODORANT

A substance used to inhibit or disguise odour.

EMOLLIENT

Used to soothe external inflammation or dryness.

EMULSIFYING WAX

An emulsifier is an agent which blends oils and water together as a homogenous mixture. There are many types of emulsifying agents but the two which I have found to be the most stable are cetomacrogol emulsifying wax and stearic acid. The latter makes a wonderful, light vanishing cream but needs the addition of triethanolamine, a substance formed from ammonia and alcohol. There are simple emulsifying agents such as beeswax, lecithin and borax with which you might like to experiment, but they don't have the same stability as cetomacrogol and stearic acid and also tend to be much heavier and greasier.

EMULSION

A mixture of oil and water which, when combined, doesn't separate. There are two types of emulsion:

WATER IN OIL: In this emulsion the oil has water packed into it as microscopically small droplets. This type of emulsion forms a cream or lotion which feels oily when first applied to the skin. Almost all creams and lotions made from ingredients such as coconut oil, beeswax and cocoa butter are water in oil emulsions and, as such, feel greasy when first applied to the skin. This needn't put you off as the greasiness is usually quickly absorbed.

OIL IN WATER: This emulsion is the reverse of the Water in Oil emulsions with the tiny droplets of oil being surrounded by water. This creates creams and lotions which feel moist but not greasy when first applied to the skin and are absorbed into the skin without leaving much or any oily residue. A 'vanishing cream' is an example of this type of emulsion. To make creams and lotions of this type it's necessary to use emulsifying waxes. These come from various natural sources (e.g. animal or vegetable fats, petroleum) or may be completely synthesised in a laboratory. The wax which I occasionally use if I want a vanishing cream is cetomacrogol emulsifying wax (described previously). If you don't feel good about using any synthetically treated products at all, you will have to settle for water in oil emulsions. I feel fine about using emulsifying wax for some of the things I make – the proportion is sometimes as low as 5% and the wax is an inert, non-allergenic ingredient which started off life as a nut on a tree. The final choice has to be yours, so I offer recipes for both types of creams and lotions.

ESSENCE
A mixture of 30ml (1fl oz) essential oils with 500ml (2 cups/16fl oz) vodka (high-proof).

ESSENTIAL OIL
The concentrated perfume of a plant obtained as an oil by various extraction methods.

EXFOLIANT
An agent used as a gentle peeling agent to rid the skin of dead cells.

GELATINE
A powdered glue-like substance, made from animal bones, hoofs and skin. Used as a thickening agent. Use agar agar (see beginning of this Glossary) if you are vegetarian and don't want to use any animal products.

GLYCERINE
A substance found in animal and vegetable fats. It is sweet, colourless, odourless and transparent, with the consistency of syrup. As a humectant it is useful in cosmetics and also serves as an antibacterial agent, softener, lubricant and preservative. In order to preserve effectively, it needs to be 20% of the total formula, which would be far too much for the average cream or lotion, but, if smaller amounts are combined with 4% tincture benzoin, together they make a good natural preservative.

HONEY
Honey cleanses, heals, softens, moisturises, hydrates and acts as a humectant. You will see from this impressive list why honey is an ingredient in so many cosmetics.

HUMECTANT
A substance with the capacity for attracting and holding moisture in the skin, for example glycerine and honey.

HYDRATE
To keep the normal fluid balance in the skin.

KAOLIN
A fine earth clay used for making porcelain, soap, paint and paper. Cosmetically, it is used as a binder in packs and scrubs. Kaolin is particularly useful for oily/combination skins as it can absorb a large amount of grease.

LANOLIN, ANHYDROUS
Also known as wool fat. This is the fat in the wool of sheep which is extracted by boiling the wool after the sheep has been shorn. This fat is very close in composition to the sebum in human skin and, because of this compatibility, lanolin is a valuable lubricant and moisturiser.

LECITHIN

An internal and external emulsifier, usually made from the soya bean. It's available in health food shops in powder, granule or liquid form. It leaves the skin with a soft sheen and a smooth texture.

LOOFAH

Those of you who haven't come across this wonderful bath aid have a treat in store. A loofah is a tropical member of the gourd family. It grows in a similar fashion to marrows and looks very similar. The sponge is the fibrous skeleton which emerges when the flesh has rotted away. The texture is quite coarse but not unpleasantly so. Used before and during a shower or bath it gets rid of dead skin and whips up the circulation to leave you glowing.

LOTION

A liquid preparation applied to the skin.

MILK

Milk is inexpensive, healing, softening and nourishing. It may be used fresh or dried and will be found useful in facials, baths, face packs and lotions. Use skim milk for oily skin, whole milk for dry or normal skin.

MOISTURISER

See Humectant.

MUCILAGE

Gummy, jelly-like substance obtained from certain plants (see also TRAGACANTH).

OATS (*AVENA SATIVA*)

To most people the word 'oats' probably conjures up a picture of bowls of steaming porridge on cold mornings; it's unlikely they would think of soft, silky skin. Oats are rich in iron, protein, potassium, magnesium and silicon and this makes them wonderfully nutritious, both internally and externally. They can be used as a bath additive, cleanser, nourisher, skin softener and exfoliant.

SALVE

A soothing, softening and healing ointment.

TONIC

A mild astringent.

TRAGACANTH (*ASTRALAGUS GUMMIFER*)

A powdered, dried gum obtained from the plant. An excellent, softening emollient which swells to a mucilage when liquid is added. It's very expensive but you need only use a little and it's a very useful thickener for creams and lotions.

VINEGAR

The word 'vinegar' is a derivation from the French *vin aigre* which means sour wine. Cider vinegar is made from apples and seems to be the best to use for cosmetic purposes. Skin is naturally acidic and because of this has the capacity to repel infection. If for some reason this acid mantle is destroyed (most soaps are alkaline) a vinegar wash or other acidic treatment (such as lemon juice) will restore the balance (see ACID/ALKALINE in this glossary).

COSMETIC BASICS

BEESWAX

Beeswax can be purchased from a pharmacy (expensive) or from a beekeeper (much cheaper). If you go direct to the beekeeper, the wax is likely to be full of strange bits and pieces. Don't worry about this as it's easy to clean.

Here is my method for cleaning and measuring wax. Buy several ice cube trays. Pour 1 tablespoon of water into one of the hollows and note the level. My trays holds exactly 1 tablespoon in each cube hollow and each cube weighs about 14g ($\frac{1}{2}$oz). You can find trays for very small cubes in which you can make teaspoon-sized blocks.

Empty the water out, dry the tray and grease it well with oil. Put the beeswax in a pan, cover with cold water and bring slowly to the boil. (Turn the heat down low at this stage as you don't want to boil the wax – just melt it.) When the wax has melted, turn the heat off and leave the contents to cool and set.

Drain off the water. Lift out the block of wax and you will see the underside has quite a thick coating of impurities. Scrape this layer off, break up the wax roughly and return it to the dry pan.

From this point on, this method can also be used for cocoa butter.

Melt the wax or butter slowly. Don't let it get too hot, or it might burn or destroy the ice cube tray when you pour it in. When the wax has melted, begin to pour. Fill each hollow in the tray to the predetermined level and leave to set. Turn the cubes out and store in a sealed container as there is a little moth that loves to feed on wax!

Weigh the cubes together before packing and divide the weight by the number of cubes. You will then know approximately how much each cube weighs, so if a recipe specifies an amount by weight you will be able to estimate easily how many cubes to use. Write the weight per cube on the outside of the storage container.

ARROWROOT OR CORNFLOUR MASK BASE

Make this jelly to suit your own needs, adding less water at first and thinning a little if you find the mixture too thick.

Slowly add 6–8 tablespoons cold water to 2 heaped teaspoons of either arrowroot or cornflour. Bring to the boil in a small pan, stirring all the time. Cool until lukewarm. Now add mashed herbs, fruit, vegetables or any other nutrient-filled mask ingredient.

OILS

To me, the word 'oils' conjures up a feeling of soft luxury, big fluffy bath towels, perfumed bodies, relaxing massage and time out to do nothing but enjoy.

Scented oils have been used by the Romans, Chinese, Egyptians and Greeks, and I imagine all the ancient civilisations used perfumed oils in many ways: embalming, anointing, baths, massage, cooking, lighting their homes and polishing furniture.

Today there is a resurgence in the use of oils. It is now recognised that essential oils massaged into the skin or inhaled are absorbed through the pores and the lungs and from there disperse rapidly through the system. Aromatherapy is the art of using pure essential oils (usually as massage oil) to treat illness, to relax, to stimulate and to help the body resist disease. Massage has become an accepted treatment for many problems and more and more people are learning the art of massage in order to share with each other a healing, relaxing and communicating experience.

There are basically two types of oils: fixed oils and volatile oils.

FIXED OILS

Classified as lipids, these are obtained from seeds and don't evaporate. The most important ones for the purpose of this book are olive, avocado, apricot, canola, castor, grape seed, safflower,

sesame, peanut, soya and wheat germ. These are the oils from which you will make creams, lotions, bath and massage oils.

There are two methods used to extract oils from their sources:

COLD PRESSING:

As the name suggests, this involves the crushing and pressing of the plant material without applying heat. It preserves the properties of the oil as well as the vitamins and minerals. Preservatives or antioxidants are not usually added – another point in its favour.

SOLVENT OR HEAT EXTRACTION:

This method destroys most of the mineral and vitamin content, and preservatives and anti-oxidants are normally added. In comparison with cold pressed oil, this oil is inferior.

OILS FOR SKIN TYPES

COMPATIBILITY OF FIXED OILS WITH SKIN TYPES

Different oils react in different ways with the skin. For instance, canola, grape seed and safflower oil are good 'all-rounders' – light, nourishing, almost dispersible in water, quickly absorbed into the skin and altogether very nice to use. Wheat germ oil acts as a preservative, so it's good to include some in all massage oils. As a rule of thumb, you will find that these oils are good for these skin types.

DRY SKIN	NORMAL SKIN	OILY SKIN
Almond	Almond	Soya bean
Canola	Canola	**Oils which are easily absorbed into the skin (use for cosmetics)**
Castor	Corn	Canola, corn, grape seed, safflower, sesame, sunflower, wheat germ.
Cocoa butter	Grape seed	**Less easily absorbed oils (use for massage oils)**
Grape seed	Peanut	Sweet almond, avocado, coconut, olive, apricot, peanut
Olive	Sesame	
Peanut	Sunflower	
Wheat germ	Safflower	

ESSENTIAL OILS/VOLATILE OILS

These are obtained from the leaves and flowers of some plants and the rinds of fruits such as orange, lemon and grapefruit. These oils are frequently called essences, essential oils or ethereal oils. They are non-greasy and evaporative. Essential oils are extracted mainly by distillation or by using alcohol.

If you are uncertain how to differentiate between essential and fixed oils, try this experiment. On a folded tissue, put a few drops of a fixed oil. In a different area, place a few drops of an essential oil and leave overnight. In the morning you will find there is a greasy patch left by the fixed oil but not by the essential oil.

These essential oils are rarely used alone. They are very powerful and are added to alcohol, water or fixed oils. With very few exceptions, they must never exceed 2–3% of the total recipe if being used directly on the skin.

There are a lot of synthetic essential oils on the market. They will smell all right but won't have the therapeutic properties of the real thing; in fact, they can be harmful. To obtain the best oils you

may have to pay a great deal of money. Rose, jasmine and ylang-ylang are among the most expensive oils and, if they aren't, then they are probably synthetic.

It takes enormous amounts of plant material to obtain a small amount of its precious essence. For instance, 100kg (220lb) of thyme leaves will yield about ¾ cup (185ml/6fl oz) of essence. This means that if you pick 1kg (2lb) of top quality leaves (which is a lot from the average garden) and use a sophisticated extraction method, you will obtain only about 2ml of essence (less than half a teaspoon)! This is not to put you off, but to illustrate how precious these oils are.

ESSENTIAL OILS

Basil	*Geranium*	*Myrrh*
Benzoin	*Ginger*	*Neroli* *(Orange Blossom)*
Bergamot	*Grapefruit*	*Orange*
Black Pepper	*Jasmine*	*Patchouli*
Cedarwood	*Juniper*	*Petitgrain*
Chamomile	*Lavender*	*Pine*
Clary Sage	*Lemon*	*Rosemary*
Clove	*Mandarin*	*Sandalwood*
Cypress	*Marjoram*	*Tea Tree*
Eucalyptus	*Melissa* *(Lemon Balm)*	*Thyme*
Fennel	*Mint, Pepper*	*Ylang-ylang*
Frankincense	*Mint, Spear*	

Basic Herb Oil

These oils can be used in massage oils, bath oils and creams. They are an essential part of many of the recipes in this chapter.

HOT METHOD

You will need a preserving thermometer for this method. An electric crock-pot or slow cooker is also an advantage.

finely chopped herbs of your choice
4 cups (1 litre/1³/4 pints) mixed peanut and
safflower or canola oil
1 tablespoon cider or wine vinegar

Place the herbs in a non-aluminium double boiler and cover with oil.

Add the vinegar, cover with a lid and leave for several hours (the vinegar will begin to extract the properties of the herbs). Heat to no more than 55°C (130°F). If hotter, some important volatile qualities of herbs will be lost. Turn off the heat.

Repeat the heating several times over a period of 24 hours.

Carefully strain the cool oil through muslin, squeezing the herbs to extract as much oil as possible. For a very strong oil, add more herbs and repeat the process once or even twice more.

After a few days some sediment will appear at the bottom of the jar. Carefully decant the oil into a clean jar or bottle, leaving the sediment behind. Refrigerate the oil until needed.

Add essential oils to this as needed.

COLD METHOD

If you live in a warm climate, you will find this method good to capture the perfume of delicate leaves and flowers. The resulting oil isn't as strong or as well coloured as obtained by the Hot Method but it is the best way to extract the scent. However, this oil is best made in the summer as you need to have strong, hot sunlight.

finely chopped herbs of your choice
4 cups (1 litre/1³/4 pints) mixed peanut and
canola or safflower oil
1 tablespoon vodka

Place the herbs in a large jar and cover with the slightly warmed oil. Add the vodka, cover with a lid and place in the sun for 1 week. (The vodka will begin to extract the properties of the herbs.)

After a few days some sediment will appear at the bottom of the jar. Carefully decant the oil into a clean jar or bottle, leaving the sediment behind. Refrigerate the oil until needed.

Add the essential oils to this as needed.

Note:
You must use purified or distilled water, as plain water is a medium for growing bacteria.

STORING YOUR BEAUTY PRODUCTS

It's easy to personalise a range of skin-care items by using the same essential oils as in your home-made perfumes. Try to find really pretty jars and bottles in which to put your 'lotions and potions', and make beautiful labels. They will then feel and look very exclusive and special. All preparations need to be tightly covered, to exclude air.

NATURAL SKIN CARE

Skin isn't just a layer to stop us fraying round the edge but a complex structure which serves us well and deserves the best treatment we can give it. Like your hair, your skin usually shows the condition of your health. Stress, lack of sleep, poor diet and illness are some of the conditions which can show in the skin.

It is a very complex organ, acting as an efficient envelope, a temperature regulator, a toxin excretor and a sensory connector between the nervous system and outside stimuli. Our skin is made up of three layers: the epidermis, the dermis and subcutaneous tissue.

EPIDERMIS

This is the outer layer, which is visible. It is made up of flattened, dead and dying cells which overlap to form an elastic, water-resistant surface. These cells are constantly being replaced by new cells from beneath, the layer being renewed every month. All the layers are gradually replaced over a period of seven years. This is very heartening as it means it's never too late to improve the condition of your skin, although you will not get back the skin you had in childhood. With age, your skin gradually loses elasticity. You can, however, slow the ageing process to a degree. Friction or exfoliant treatments help to rid your skin of dead cells more quickly, allowing new cells to move up.

DERMIS

This layer produces the new cells which make their way up to the epidermis. The dermis contains oil glands, blood vessels, hair follicles and nerves and is connected to the epidermis by collagen fibres.

SUBCUTANEOUS TISSUE

This is a fatty layer which gives a protective pad to underlying bone and organs and also contains sweat glands.

To keep your skin in the best possible condition, there are a few simple steps you can take. The rest is up to nature!

◆ Eat lots of fruit and vegetables

◆ Drink 6–8 glasses of water daily.

◆ Get 6–8 hours sleep a night

◆ Do some form of exercise daily, whatever you enjoy

◆ Use the purest skin preparations that you can make or buy

◆ Keep out of the sun during the hottest part of the day and use a good sunblock whenever you are outside in the summer

◆ If you play sport or are out of doors a lot, make sure you use plenty of moisturiser to protect your skin

◆ Cultivate a positive attitude. Stress is about the worst thing for skin, giving that lined, drawn look. I teach meditation and always notice the astonishing difference in people's faces after a class. They can look years younger and softer.

SKIN TYPES

There are four main skin types:

NORMAL SKIN

Alas, rarely seen. It is fine-textured, smooth, supple and soft, with no blackheads or spots. This skin should be cherished and maintained with light cleansers, lotions and tonics or fresheners.

OILY SKIN

The texture is usually thick, coarse and shiny. Large pores are a characteristic of this type of skin. There is a tendency to blackheads and spots due to the over-excretion of oil with its clogging tendencies. Take heart if you have oily skin. It wrinkles less and later than any other type. This skin needs plenty of moisture and little oil, except on the throat and lips and around the eyes. Use astringent face packs, tonics and treatments to give a good acid mantle.

COMBINATION SKIN

As the name suggests, this is a combination of normal or dry and oily skin. The oily areas are usually across the forehead and down the nose to the chin; sometimes there are small areas on the jawline. This skin needs 2 different programmes, oily and normal or oily and dry.

DRY SKIN

The skin is fine-textured, thin and delicate. It has a tendency to line easily. If neglected, the skin flakes and feels tight and uncomfortable. Hot packs and steams need to be avoided as they encourage the broken veins to which this type of skin is prone.

It's good to develop a skin-care routine to keep the skin in good condition. This needn't be time-consuming but is as necessary as cleaning your teeth. Two factors determine the number of times a day you need to follow this routine: the work you do (whether dusty or clean), and whether you live in the city with polluted air or in the country. If you spend much time in air-conditioned rooms, your skin will need more moisturising.

The way you apply treatments to your face and throat is very important. Remember that skin loses its elasticity as it gets older, so use two fingers only, in gentle, non-stretching movements. Gravity is working against us as well, in an effort to pull everything towards the ground, so always use upward movements in an effort to counteract this.

CARING FOR YOUR FACE

CLEANSING

If you have oily skin or work in a dirty environment, you will need to cleanse at least twice a day. If your skin is normal or dry, then once a day should be sufficient. The evening is the best time to cleanse, to rid the skin of the grime and oil accumulated during the day. The aim of cleansing is to rid the skin of excess grease, dead skin cells and dirt. Some people don't feel clean unless they have used soap and water on their face. This is fine if you are careful to use good quality soap and then follow with a rinse designed to restore the skin's natural acid balance. For those who don't like soap (many people prefer not to use it on their faces), you can use oil, cleansing cream or lotion. Recipes for various types of cleansers are given.

SOAPS

Soap-making from scratch is quite tricky as you need to use caustic, which can burn badly if it is splashed onto skin. For most people, it is easier and safer to use ready-made soap as the base and these recipes use this method. Buy the simplest, least expensive soap in your supermarket, preferably unperfumed and with no fancy additives. It tends to be the ideal base to make a range of soaps which are inexpensive, cleansing, moisturising, sweetly scented and always such a pleasure to use.

The amount of infusion or decoction needed in these recipes varies because the soap you buy can contain varying amounts of water.

Lemon and Corn Soap

SUITS OILY AND COMBINATION SKINS

4 cups (400g/12$^{1}/_{2}$oz) very finely grated soap
$^{1}/_{2}$–1 cup (125–250ml/4–8fl oz) hot Triple Strength Infusion or decoction of your favourite herbs, strained
1 tablespoon glycerine
$^{1}/_{4}$ cup (40g/1$^{1}/_{2}$oz) polenta
$^{1}/_{2}$ teaspoon lemon essential oil

Melt the soap into the infusion or decoction and glycerine in a double boiler. Cool until lukewarm, add the polenta and essential oil and work in well.

Form into balls or press into greased moulds such as soap boxes, small jelly moulds or baskets lined with cheesecloth. The soap will dry more quickly if plenty of air can circulate around it. Drying time will be about 6 weeks.

Honey and Glycerine Soap

SUITS ALL SKINS

If you have very fine, dry skin, use this soap on your body. I use orange peel, comfrey and mallow root decoction and add orange oil to finish. The soap smells and feels wonderful on my skin.

4 cups (400g/12$^{1}/_{2}$oz) finely grated soap
2 teaspoons glycerine
2 teaspoons honey
$^{1}/_{2}$–1 cup (125–250ml/4–8fl oz) hot Triple Strength Infusion or decoction of your favourite herbs, strained
$^{1}/_{2}$ teaspoon essential oil

Melt the soap, glycerine and honey in a double boiler with the infusion or decoction. Cool until lukewarm and add the essential oil, mixing in very well.

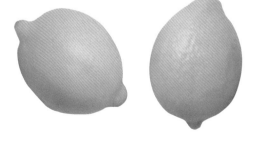

Honey Gel

GOOD FOR ALL SKIN TYPES

1 level teaspoon tragacanth
2²/₃ cups (660ml/22fl oz) purified water
4¹/₂ level teaspoons gelatine
5 level teaspoons honey
¹/₂ cup (125ml/4fl oz) glycerine
5 teaspoons vodka
4 teaspoons liquid castile soap
16 drops essential oil
5 drops tincture benzoin

Mix tragacanth to a thin paste with a little of the water. Heat the remaining water, then sprinkle on the gelatine and stir to dissolve. Slowly add to the tragacanth mixture, stirring, then strain.

Stir in the remaining ingredients and bottle. Invert the bottle occasionally while cooling, to mix in the oil.

This gel will keep in the refrigerator for several weeks.

To use, wet your face first. Squeeze a little mixture into the palm of your hand and massage gently onto your face, working up a lather. Splash cool water on your face to remove the cleanser. Blot dry.

This cleanser doesn't really need a toner but you could follow with a vinegar splash if you like (see Toning). For a real 'zing', use peppermint oil as the essential oil.

Cleansing Balm

This rich cleanser leaves normal, dry or combination skins feeling very soft. Use a skin tonic after this cream.

1 cube (14g/¹/₂oz) beeswax
1 tablespoon coconut oil
¹/₄ cup (60ml/2fl oz) Basic Herb Oil
1 tablespoon herb infusion
¹/₂ teaspoon borax
10 drops tincture benzoin
10 drops essential oil

Melt the beeswax in a small pan over low heat, then melt in the coconut oil and gently stir in the herb oil. Remove from the heat and cool until lukewarm, so that the mixture does not set.

Dissolve the herb infusion and borax together and beat into the oil mixture, then beat in the remaining ingredients until well mixed. Spoon into a clean jar. Keeps well with refrigeration except in very hot weather.

SCRUBS

These are used to peel ('exfoliate') the outer, dead layer of skin. This needs to be done gently and not too often. It can leave your skin silky soft, glowing and looking much younger. Scrubs should be applied to a previously cleansed and wet face. Avoid the delicate area around the eyes.

Herb Scrub

1 part ground rice
2 parts ground herbs

Mix well and store in a closed jar.

Add a little milk to a small portion of the herb scrub and mix to a paste. Put a little in the palm of your hand and massage onto moistened skin with circular motions. Splash off with cool water.

Mealy Scrub

Mix up the dry ingredients for this recipe in bulk and store it in an airtight container until needed.

For the basic dry mix, you will need 4 parts oatmeal, 1 part fine cornmeal, 2 parts ground almonds, ¹/₂ part kaolin and ¹/₂ part raw sugar.

1 teaspoon honey
1 teaspoon glycerine
2 drops essential oil
basic dry mix
water to mix

Mix the honey, glycerine and oil together in a small bowl. Blend in 1–2 teaspoons of the dry mix and enough water to make a soft paste.

Wet your face, put a little mixture into the palm of your hand and massage the scrub onto the skin with your fingers in a gentle, circular motion. Splash off with cool water.

TONING

Toning helps to refine skin texture. It's also essential where heavy cleansers have been used, in order to rid the pores of excess grease which could clog and cause blackheads. The type of toner you use is determined by the method you have used to cleanse.

Cosmetic Vinegar

I choose a variety of herbs that will be useful for many functions as I use this vinegar as a deodorant, hair rinse, skin tonic, wound wash and bath additive. The dilution rate is a matter of personal preference. I would never use more than 2 teaspoons in a cup of water as a facial rinse or after-shower splash, but would use it neat as a deodorant. Your skin type also determines the dilution, oily skins being able to tolerate a much stronger mix.

60g (2oz) herbs
2 cups (500ml/16fl oz) cider vinegar
1 tablespoon glycerine

Chop or mash the herbs very finely. Heat half the vinegar to just below boiling point, then immediately add the herbs. Pour into a jar, leave for a week, then strain through double cheese-cloth and add the remaining vinegar.

Add the glycerine, then bottle. It keeps well without refrigeration except in very hot weather.

Cucumber Tonic

ALL SKINS

If your skin is oily you should peel the cucumber. If dry or normal, leave unpeeled. The main astringent content is in the flesh. This is a lovely, light, refreshing toner. If you live in a hot climate, keep cubes in the freezer to wipe one over your face on hot days. It gets rid of that sticky feeling.

1 medium cucumber
6 teaspoons witch hazel extract
3 teaspoons distilled water
1 teaspoon essential oil

Blend the cucumber to a pulp, strain twice through double cheesecloth, add the remaining ingredients, strain once more and bottle. This needs refrigeration and will keep for only a few days but it freezes well.

Herbal Tonic

ALL SKIN TYPES, DEPENDING ON HERBS USED

This tonic can be made using the same herbs and essential oils as for your cleanser and moisturiser.

$1/4$ cup (60ml/2fl oz) double strength infusion or decoction of your favourite herbs, double-strained through coffee filter paper
$1/4$ cup (60ml/2fl oz) witch hazel extract
$1/2$ teaspoon glycerine
5 drops tincture benzoin
5 drops essential oil

Mix all the ingredients well and bottle. Shake well before using. This needs refrigeration and will keep for only a few days.

MOISTURISING

All skin needs water as well as oil in order to remain soft and supple. If water is just splashed onto the skin it evaporates before it can be absorbed, so it needs an additional agent to hold it on the skin until absorption takes place. Some of these agents are oil, glycerine or honey. Moisturising can be done as often as you like. You will be able to tell by the feel of your skin when you need more.

Most of the recipes in this section are emulsions of oil and water. Some feel greasy when you first apply them and some do not. See which you prefer.

Green Gunk is nourishing for all skins. It is suitable for men, women and children. Children's skin needs protection as much as adults' if the climate is harsh, but this protection needs to be very light and non-clogging to those fine pores.

Green Gunk

My grandchildren named this preparation! It's basically a mayonnaise, although the taste isn't as good as the action. It moisturises, feeds, balances and leaves your skin soft. As well as a moisturiser, you can use it as a pre-shampoo treatment, bath oil, after-shower skin oil or hand cream. For really chapped hands, you can put it on thickly, cover with cotton gloves and then with plastic ones and go to bed. Or you can massage it in gently while you listen to music or watch television.

2 egg yolks
1 tablespoon Herb Vinegar
2 cups (500ml/16fl oz) herb oil
2 tablespoons plain yoghurt
1 teaspoon essential oil

Beat the egg yolks and vinegar in a blender until well mixed, then add the oil slowly until the mixture is very thick. Mix the remaining ingredients in very well. Store in the refrigerator, where it will keep for several weeks.

Almond and Glycerine Moisture Lotion

Apply a little of this lotion after cleansing. Smooth into the skin until absorbed. It needs refrigeration and will keep for only a few days, but freezes well.

$^1/_2$ cup (125ml/4fl oz) purified water
2 tablespoons ground almonds
$^1/_4$ medium cucumber, chopped
$^3/_4$ cup (185ml/6fl oz) water
10 drops tincture benzoin
2 teaspoons glycerine

Boil the purified water and pour over the almonds in a bowl. Cover and leave for 2 hours.

Combine the cucumber and water in a saucepan, bring to the boil, turn the heat off and allow to cool. Add to the almond mixture and strain all through double cheesecloth.

Add the remaining ingredients and mix well. Store in a bottle in the refrigerator.

Orange Moisture Lotion or Night Cream

This is a lovely moisturiser, rich and creamy, and good for dry, normal and combination skins. Very little is needed. Massage gently into the skin until absorbed. It may feel a little greasy but is very soothing, especially to dry skin. In very hot weather, it may separate, so shake well until blended again. It is particluarly good with orange peel used in the infusion and basic oil mix.

1 cube (14g/$^1/_2$oz) beeswax
1 tablespoon coconut oil
$^1/_2$ cube (7g/$^1/_4$oz) cocoa butter
$^1/_2$ cup (125ml/4fl oz) Basic Herb Oil
$^1/_2$ cup Triple Strength Infusion
$^1/_2$ teaspoon borax
15 drops orange oil

Melt the wax in a small pan over simmering water or in a double boiler. Add the coconut oil and cocoa butter, stir until melted, then slowly add the basic oil, stirring. Take off the heat.

Dissolve the borax in the infusion, strain and add slowly to the oil mixture, stirring and heating again if necessary to 45°C (113°F).

Stir in the orange oil and bottle. Shake the bottle occasionally until the mixture is cold.

PRESERVING CREAMS

Using a little more infusion will give you a lotion rather than a cream. Experiment until you find which is the best for your skin. You can preserve these creams for a longer shelf life.

The preservatives which I have used successfully and with no reported ill effects are chlorocresol and phenoxitol. They are not as strong as many used by commercial cosmetic manufacturers but were recommended to me by two very reputable pharmaceutical chemists, and a dermatologist who uses them in ointments and creams for skin. They are both water miscible.

Caution:

The recommended proportions need to be adhered to very precisely and must never be exceeded: phenoxitol is used at a concentration of 1% (that is 1g to every 99g of other ingredients); chlorocresol is used at a concentration of 0.1% (that is $^1/_{10}$th of a gram (1mg) to 99.9g of other ingredients).

Lemon Cream

SUITS OILY OR COMBINATION SKINS

This is a lovely moisturiser which won't make your skin feel greasy. Use lemon peel and/or lemon grass in the infusion and the Basic Herb Oil.

30g (1oz) cetomacrogol emulsifying wax
2 teaspoons Basic Herb Oil
$^3/_4$ cup (185ml/6fl oz) infusion or decoction of your favourite herbs
3 teaspoons glycerine
2.4ml (a bare $^1/_2$ teaspoon) phenoxitol (optional)
1 teaspoon tincture benzoin
18 drops essential oil

Melt the wax and oil together in small double boiler and heat to 65°C (149°F).

Heat the infusion or decoction, glycerine and phenoxitol together in separate pan to 70°C (158°F). Pour onto wax and oil and stir continuously until it is 45°C (113°F). Add the remaining ingredients, mix in well and pour into jars. This will keep refrigerated for several weeks.

Aloe and Comfrey Moisture Cream

SUITS DRY, NORMAL OR COMBINATION SKINS

This cream is also very good to use as a burn soother. It will keep refrigerated for several weeks.

To make aloe juice, scrape the gel from the inside of the leaf and put it into a blender. Blend to a juicy pulp, adding a little distilled water if necessary. The pulp will be very glutinous. Put it into a pan and heat it to boiling point, taking care not to burn the pulp. Cool and strain the juice.

30g (1oz) cetomacrogol emulsifying wax
1 tablespoon Basic Herb Oil (using comfrey)
$^3/_4$ cup (185ml/6fl oz) aloe juice (see above)
1 tablespoon glycerine
2.4ml (a bare $^1/_2$ teaspoon) phenoxitol (optional)
1 teaspoon tincture benzoin
15–18 drops essential oil

Melt the wax and oil together in small double boiler and heat to 65°C (149°F).

Heat the aloe juice, glycerine and phenoxitol together in a separate pan to 70°C (158°F), then pour onto the wax and oil, stirring continuously until it is 45°C (113°F). Add the remaining ingredients, mix in well and pour into jars.

Hand Lotion

This lotion keeps well without refrigeration except in very hot weather.

1 teaspoon witch hazel extract
2 teaspoons glycerine
5 teaspoons cologne (see Colognes Using Essential Oils)

Mix all the ingredients together. Apply a few drops and massage in well.

STEAM TREATMENTS

In addition to your daily programme, facial steams can be an occasional treat. Steaming is really a deep-cleansing treatment for the skin. It whips up the circulation, adds moisture and softens the grease in clogged pores, making blackheads easier to remove. Never use facial steaming if you have broken capillary or 'thread' veins, as the heat aggravates the condition, but all other skins benefit from this treatment. It can be used monthly if your skin is dry or sensitive, fortnightly for normal skin and once or twice weekly for skin with very clogged pores or excessive grease.

To take a steam treatment, tie your hair back with a shower cap or head band and cleanse your face in the usual manner. Now chop two handfuls of herbs of your choice, place in a basin and pour 8 cups (2 litres/$3^{1}/_{2}$ pints) of boiling water over the herbs. Holding your face about 20cm (8in) away from the steam, cover your head and the basin with a large towel, forming a sort of tent. Keep your eyes closed and let the steam play on your face for about 10 minutes (you can come up for air occasionally if you need to). Finish the steaming session with a lukewarm water (not cold) splash.

Herbs for Facial Steams

FOR DRY SKIN:
Use chamomile, comfrey, elderflower, mallow root or red clover.

FOR NORMAL SKIN:
Use chamomile, comfrey, fennel or red clover.

FOR OILY SKIN:
Use anise, fennel, lavender, lemon grass, marjoram, plantain, raspberry or yarrow.

FOR BLACKHEADS:
Use bay, fennel, lemon grass or nasturtium.

MASKS

Masks can cleanse, tone, moisturise, exfoliate, refine, heal and nourish. They are fun to make and use, leave your skin feeling and looking years younger and give you an excuse to lie down for a while. Before you use a mask, you need to cleanse your face thoroughly.

Tie your hair back as for steaming and spread the mixture on your face. If you find the mixture too sloppy, you can make a poultice (see Poultices), for the size of your face and throat, to contain the ingredients. Don't apply the mask mixture to the delicate area around your eyes. Now lie down and relax for 15–20 minutes. The mask will stay in place better if you are horizontal and will work better if you are relaxed. Then wash it off with lukewarm water.

Masks can be thickened with all sorts of things from your kitchen cupboard and refrigerator: leftover porridge, dried milk, the cooked arrowroot or cornflour base (see Masks), wheat germ, ground almonds, mashed banana or cooked pumpkin.

Green Herb Mask

SUITABLE FOR ALL SKIN TYPES, DEPENDING
ON THE HERBS CHOSEN

2 handfuls fresh herbs, finely chopped
2 tablespoons purified water
1 teaspoon honey
wheat germ

Blend or mash the herbs, water and honey together until pulpy and very fine, then add enough wheat germ to make a soft paste.

Pat onto your face and throat and lie down for 10–20 minutes.

Oily Skin Mask

1 tablespoon dried and powdered lemon grass
$^1/_4$ teaspoon brewer's yeast
1 tablespoon plain yoghurt
kaolin or oat flour

Mix together the lemon grass, yeast and yoghurt in a bowl, then add enough kaolin or flour to form a soft paste.

Pat onto your face and throat and leave for 10–20 minutes. Rinse off with lukewarm water and apply moisturiser.

Mask for Dry or Delicate Skin

3 tablespoons aloe pulp
1 teaspoon honey, melted
almond meal

Scrape the pulp from inside the aloe leaves and blend the aloe pulp with the honey, then add enough almond meal to make a soft paste.

Smooth over your face and neck and leave for 10–20 minutes. Rinse off with warm water and apply moisturiser.

Arrowroot Mask

SUITS ALL SKIN TYPES

This is a very useful mask as the honey and glycerine attract and hold moisture in the skin. By choosing your own herbs, this recipe can be adapted for any skin type or problem. For a thicker or thinner mask, vary the amount of arrowroot. The mixture thickens as it cools.

2 teaspoons arrowroot
2 teaspoons honey
$^3/_4$ cup (185ml/6fl oz) double strength infusion
or decoction of your favourite herbs
1 teaspoon Basic Herb Oil

Mix the arrowroot and honey to a paste with a little of the infusion in a saucepan, then mix in the remaining infusion and cook, stirring, until thickened. Cool.

Add the herb oil. Smooth over your face and neck and leave for 15 minutes. Rinse off and apply moisturiser. Keeps well without refrigeration except in very hot weather.

NATURAL SKIN CARE CHART

Instructions for the following treatments will be found in these sections:
Cleansing; Masks; Steam Treatments; Moisturising; Toning.

TO CARE FOR NORMAL SKIN

◆ Cleanse with chamomile, dandelion, elderflower, honey, dried milk, oatmeal or sage
◆ Deep cleanse with masks containing aloe vera, anise, caraway, castor oil, chamomile, elderflower, fennel, honey, lavender*, dried milk, oatmeal, egg yolk, parsley, plain yoghurt , vinegar
◆ Steam with chamomile, comfrey root, fennel or red clover
◆ Nourish with moisturisers and masks of aloe vera, comfrey root, egg, plain yoghurt or honey
◆ Tone with calendula, chamomile, comfrey root, dandelion, elderflower, lavender*, lemon balm, lemon grass, lemon juice, witch hazel extract, yarrow* or cider vinegar

TO CARE FOR DRY SKIN

◆ Cleanse with chamomile, dandelion, elderflower, honey, lemon balm, lemon grass, dried milk, oatmeal
◆ Deep cleanse with masks containing aloe vera, anise, castor oil, chamomile, egg yolk, elderflower, fennel, full cream dried milk, honey, oatmeal, parsley or plain yoghurt
◆ Steam with chamomile, comfrey root, elderflower, mallow root, red clover
◆ Nourish with moisturisers and masks of aloe root, comfrey and mallow root, egg yolk, honey
◆ Tone with borage, chamomile, marjoram, elderflower, cider vinegar, rosewater

TO CARE FOR SENSITIVE SKIN

◆ Cleanse with chamomile, elderflower, honey, full cream dried milk, oatmeal
◆ Steam with chamomile, comfrey root, fennel, red clover
◆ Nourish with moisturisers and masks of aloe vera, comfrey root, honey
◆ Tone with aloe vera, chamomile, comfrey or mallow root, rosewater

TO CARE FOR OILY SKIN

◆ Cleanse with borage, elderflower, honey, marjoram, parsley, peppermint, raspberry, oatmeal, sage
◆ Deep cleanse with masks of bergamot, catnep, dandelion, fennel, honey, lavender*, lemon grass, lemon juice, marjoram, skim dried milk, brewers yeast, oatmeal, plantain, sage, whole egg, yarrow*, parsley
◆ Steam with anise, fennel, lavender*, lemon grass, marjoram, plantain, raspberry, yarrow*, red clover
◆ Nourish with moisturisers and masks of aloe vera, comfrey, honey
◆ Tone with bay, bergamot, calendula, fennel, lavender*, lemon balm, lemon grass, lemon juice, thyme, witch hazel extract, yarrow*, cider vinegar

BLACKHEADS

Never attempt to squeeze blackheads until the skin is soft, moist and warm — as after one of the following treatments. Use a special tool for extracting blackheads or cover your nails with cotton wool before squeezing.

REMEDY

a) Bay, fennel, lemon grass, nasturtium
b) Oatmeal
c) Rosemary

HOW TO USE

a) Steam with a blend of the herbs
b) Scrub (see SCRUBS)
c) Mask (see MASKS)

BLEMISHES AND SPOTS

REMEDY

a) Aloe vera, bay, bergamot, calendula, lavender*, lemon balm, nasturtium, thyme
b) Roasted dandelion root
c) Honey

HOW TO USE

a) Make a Triple Strength Infusion of at least 3 of the herbs. Use 3 times daily as a face wash and skin tonic.
b) Drink 3 times a day as a tea and coffee substitute to cleanse the system.
c) Dab directly on spots.

TIRED EYES

REMEDY

a) Catnep
b) Fennel, chamomile

HOW TO USE

a) Double strength infusion applied as a cool compress.
b) Eyewash (see EYE BATHS)

VEINS, 'BROKEN'

REMEDY

Borage, calendula, chamomile

HOW TO USE

Make a Triple Strength Infusion and apply daily as a cool compress.

Caution:
Overuse of lavender and yarrow can cause skin to become sensitive to sunlight, making it more likely to pigment, often unevenly.

CARE OF YOUR MOUTH

Herbal products can help you keep your mouth sweet and your lips in good condition. In addition to the following recipes, you will find that bergamot, fennel, lavender and lemon grass are good for a mouthwash, while you can heal mouth ulcers with eucalyptus and tea tree oils.

Lip Salve

This salve will heal and soothe chapped lips and, used regularly, will keep lips soft and unlined even in harsh weather conditions. It keeps well without refrigeration except in very hot weather.

1 cube (14g/^{1}/$_2$oz) beeswax
^{1}/$_2$ cube (7g/^{1}/$_4$oz) cocoa butter
^{1}/$_4$ cup (60ml/2fl oz) Basic Herb Oil
(using calendula)
1 teaspoon glycerine
10 drops orange or mandarin oil

Melt the beeswax in a small pan over a low heat, then add the cocoa butter and melt very gently.

Mix in the base oil. Take off the heat and cool until lukewarm. Mix in the glycerine and orange or mandarin oil and pot in tiny jars.

Breath Sweetener Mouthwash

A delicious mouthwash. Use fresh herbs if possible.

2 cups (500ml/16fl oz) sherry
1 teaspoon finely chopped spearmint
1 teaspoon finely chopped peppermint
1 teaspoon finely chopped lemon thyme
1 teaspoon finely chopped sage
4 cloves, bruised
1 teaspoon ground cinnamon

Measure the sherry in a very clean jug.

Put herbs and spices into a bottle and top up with the sherry. Cork and store in a dark, cool place for 2 weeks. Strain, filter and rebottle.

HAIR CARE

When I was a child we washed our hair with soap and rainwater, finishing off with a herbal vinegar rinse. I have photographs of myself with strong, glossy brown hair (totally straight and not blonde, which was the great grief of my life) and I remember brushing my mother's hair, so black and shiny that it looked polished. Conditioners, permanent waves, hair colorants from a bottle and even 'bought' shampoos weren't heard of and yet most people, unless they were sick, had a good head of hair.

These days, shampoos and conditioners are big business, making millions for the companies who produce them. The average commercial shampoo is so damaging to your hair that you have to use a conditioner to make your hair behave. The cheaper shampoos are made to formulae very similar to dishwashing liquid or carpet shampoo. They strip the hair of all the natural oils and weaken it. Conditioners add a wax or similar coating to the hair, giving a false illusion of thickness, gloss and health.

It takes a little perseverance to get your hair back to its natural state. It could be as long as three weeks before the wax coating is completely removed from the hair shaft and the herbs can begin to show what they can do.

Hair care, like skin care, starts from the inside. Our hair is one of the first indications if all is not well. Stress, inadequate nutrition, lack of sleep and illness are some of the conditions which cause hair to fall out or to become dull and lustreless. Here are some suggestions to help you to retain or regain a fine head of hair.

The food you eat and your inner health are the main factors governing the strength and appearance of your hair.

TIPS FOR HEALTHY HAIR

◆ Use the best pure bristle brush you can afford – nylon and plastic are very hard on the hair, causing it to split.

◆ Resist the urge to shampoo more than once a week. Oiliness is made worse by frequent shampooing as it stimulates the oil glands.

◆ Use a natural, home-made shampoo from one of the recipes below or, failing this, use the best health food store shampoo that you can afford.

◆ Follow your shampoo with a herbal rinse. The use of a 'non-oily' herb oil will add a sheen and enhance the appearance, smell and health of your hair. Recipes are given below.

◆ Don't do anything rough to your hair while it is wet. After shampooing, lightly towel (or rub with a piece of silk for high sheen) and run your fingers through to arrange it. Wait until it is much drier before doing anything else. Wet hair is very elastic and can be badly stretched and weakened by rough treatment.

◆ Use hair dryers as infrequently as possible and never on a high heat. This can cause weakening and damage by making the hair brittle, dull and lifeless.

◆ Pay special attention to your hair in summer. The sea and sun can wreak havoc and you can end the season with dry, brittle, lifeless hair. Rinse well after swimming and wear a hat or scarf if you are out of doors for long periods of time. Use a pre-shampoo oil treatment at least once a fortnight.

YOU NEED THESE NUTRIENTS EVERY DAY

NUTRIENT	SOME SOURCES
INOSITOL	Beans, grains, nuts, citrus fruit, corn
PANTOTHENIC ACID	Peanuts, wheat germ, brewer's yeast, brown rice
PABA	Yeast and wheat germ
RIBOFLAVIN	Avocadoes, dairy products, yeast, wholegrain cereals
VITAMIN F	Brown rice, wheat germ, oatmeal, almonds, peanuts
SILICON	Sunflower seeds, oats, dark lettuce leaves, parsnips
PHOSPHORUS	Seeds, grains, beans, nuts, oats, wheat germ

CHOOSING HERBS FOR HAIR

ACID BALANCE

REMEDY: Cider vinegar

HOW TO USE: Add 1 tablespoon to 4 cups (1 litre/1¾ pints) warm water or herbal infusion. Use as final rinse (see A PROGRAMME FOR HEALTHY HAIR).

CLEANSING

REMEDY: Bay, clover, lemon balm, lemon grass, thyme

HOW TO USE: Add Triple Strength Infusions of all or some of the herbs to shampoo (see A PROGRAMME FOR HEALTHY HAIR).

CONDITIONING

REMEDY: Lavender, nettle, lemon grass, rosemary, sage

HOW TO USE: Add Triple Strength Infusions of some or all the herbs to shampoos and rinses (see A PROGRAMME FOR HEALTHY HAIR).

DANDRUFF

REMEDY: a) Nettle, rosemary
b) Comfrey and mallow root, willow bark, cider vinegar

HOW TO USE: a) Make a hair tonic (see A PROGRAMME FOR HEALTHY HAIR). Rub into the scalp twice a day.
b) Make Triple Strength Decoctions and add to shampoo and rinse (see A PROGRAMME FOR HEALTHY HAIR). Add 1 tablespoon cider vinegar to each litre (1¾ pints) of rinse.

DARK HAIR

REMEDY: Nettle, rosemary, sage and thyme

HOW TO USE: Add Triple Strength Infusions to shampoo, final rinse, tonic (see A PROGRAMME FOR HEALTHY HAIR) to restore and enrich colour.

DRY HAIR

REMEDY: a) Pre-shampoo treatment (see A PROGRAMME FOR HEALTHY HAIR)
b) Comfrey root, mallow root, orange peel
c) Chamomile, elderflower, lavender

HOW TO USE: a) See A PROGRAMME FOR HEALTHY HAIR.
b) Use Triple Strength Decoctions in shampoo (see A PROGRAMME FOR HEALTHY HAIR).
c) Use Triple Strength Infusions in rinse (see A PROGRAMME FOR HEALTHY HAIR).

DRY SCALP

REMEDY: Comfrey root, mallow root, nettle

HOW TO USE: Make a tonic (see A PROGRAMME FOR HEALTHY HAIR) using the above herbs. Massage into the scalp twice daily.

FALLING HAIR

REMEDY: Nettle, rosemary, southernwood, thyme, wormwood

HOW TO USE: Make a tonic (see A PROGRAMME FOR HEALTHY HAIR) using the herbs. Massage into the scalp twice daily.

FRAGRANCE

REMEDY: Basil, lavender, lemon balm, lemon grass, lemon peel, orange peel, rosemary, thyme

HOW TO USE: Make a Triple Strength Infusion of as many of the herbs as possible. Add to shampoo and rinse (see A PROGRAMME FOR HEALTHY HAIR).

FAIR HAIR

REMEDY: Chamomile, calendula

HOW TO USE: Use a Triple Strength Infusion of either or both of the herbs in shampoo and rinse (see A PROGRAMME FOR HEALTHY HAIR).

NORMAL HAIR

REMEDY: Basil, bay, comfrey root, clover, lavender, lemon balm, nettle, southernwood, wormwood

HOW TO USE: Use a combination of some or all the herbs as Triple Strength Infusions in both shampoos and rinses (see A PROGRAMME FOR HEALTHY HAIR).

OILY HAIR

REMEDY: Lemon grass, lemon peel, willow bark, witch hazel extract

HOW TO USE: Use a combination of some or all of the herbs as Triple Strength Infusions in both shampoo and rinse (see A PROGRAMME FOR HEALTHY HAIR).

SCALP IRRITATION

REMEDY: a) Chamomile, comfrey root, mallow root
b) Bay, elder flower, parsley, rosemary, southernwood, wormwood, cider vinegar

HOW TO USE: a) Make a Triple Strength Infusion of chamomile and a Triple Strength Decoction of comfrey and mallow. Use to shampoo the hair, massaging the scalp well.
b) Use the herbs for a rinse and tonic (see A PROGRAMME FOR HEALTHY HAIR). Add 1 tablespoon cider vinegar to each litre (1¾ pints) of rinse.

SHINY HAIR

REMEDY: Calendula, chamomile, lemon peel, nettle, rosemary, sage

HOW TO USE: Use as many herbs as possible in the final rinse (see A PROGRAMME FOR HEALTHY HAIR).

A PROGRAMME FOR HEALTHY HAIR

Pre-shampoo Treatment

Use this treatment about once a month. If your hair is overbleached, overpermed or otherwise dry and lustreless it may be used every week.

1 beaten egg
1 teaspoon glycerine
1 tablespoon safflower or olive oil

Mix all the ingredients well together in a bowl.

To use the treatment: massage into your hair and scalp. Cover your head with a shower cap and wrap in a hot towel.

Leave for one hour, reheating the towel occasionally. Shampoo, rinse, shampoo again, rinse again.

Protein Treatment

Use lukewarm water to shampoo this out or you will end up with scrambled eggs in your hair!

1 beaten egg
1 teaspoon glycerine
1 tablespoon safflower oil

Mix all the ingredients together in a bowl and massage into your hair and scalp as described above.

OIL TREATMENT

Choose a Basic Herb Oil to suit your hair type. Warm the oil slightly before massaging in as described above. You can also use the recipe for 'Green Gunk' in the same way, as a treatment for your hair.

SHAMPOOS

First, you need to look at which herbs best suit your hair. You might have fair hair which is in poor condition and which is also very dry. You don't have to use every herb listed, just select from those which apply. Even one herb is better than no herbs at all. Use your chosen herbs in any of the shampoos or treatments described.

Dry Shampoo

You can use a dry shampoo to remove excess oil or if, for some reason, you can't wash your hair. Sprinkle 1 teaspoon of cornmeal, oatmeal, orris root or bran through your hair and massage into the scalp. Brush out well. The more you wash your hair, the oilier it will become as you over-stimulate the sebaceous glands.

Health Food Store Shampoo

You will need the bottle of shampoo you have bought, plus an empty bottle. Empty one-quarter of the shampoo into the empty bottle. Save for another time.

Put 4 heaped teaspoons dried (or 8 teaspoons fresh) herbs into a pan with 1 cup (250ml/8fl oz) water. Cover and simmer very gently for 10 minutes. Allow to stand for 30 minutes.

Strain, pour back into the pan and simmer until enough remains to top up the three-quarters-full bottle. Cool the liquid before adding to the bottle. Shake very gently to mix well.

I use a mixture of half herbs and half shampoo because I don't mind the thin consistency and want as much herbal content as possible. Try for yourself and see which proportion you like best.

Castile Shampoo

Make a herbal infusion as for the health food store shampoo, opposite. Add to the liquid castile soap (available from health food stores) in the proportion $^1/_4$ infusion to $^3/_4$ soap. Bottle your real herbal soap and enjoy!

If you choose to make and use this shampoo you will need a vinegar rinse to restore the acid balance to your hair. Castile soap-shampoos are best for your hair, but can take a bit of getting used to as they don't feel at all like conventional shampoos. Give them a month's trial and your patience will be rewarded.

To Make a Hair Rinse

Make 4 cups (1 litre/1$^3/_4$ pints) of a Triple Strength Infusion of as many as possible of the herbs suggested in the individual remedies. Put a bowl in the washbasin and pour the cooled infusion over your head, catching the surplus in the bowl. Empty it back into the jug and repeat as often as you like.

To Make a Hair Tonic

This tonic will keep for 3–4 weeks in the refrigerator but some of it may be frozen to extend the life.
Herbs to Use: Basil, clover, lavender, lemon grass, nettle, rosemary, southernwood, thyme, wormwood.
To Make the Tonic: Make a Triple Strength Infusion using as many as possible of the above herbs. Strain into a jug.

For every 2 cups (500ml/16fl oz) of infusion add 3 teaspoons borax and dissolve. Add 40 drops lavender oil and 40 drops rosemary oil. Bottle and shake well.
To Use: shake the bottle well, apply a few drops to your scalp and, using the pads of the fingers, massage in briskly with a zig-zag movement. Don't pull your hair while massaging. Use once or twice a day.

Hair Oil

This oil will give health and sheen to your hair without making it greasy. It also gives your hair a wonderful, natural fragrance.

Mix together equal parts of rosemary, lavender and either basil or juniper oils with jojoba oil. Put a few drops on the palm of one hand and rub your hands together. Now rub the oil from your palms through your hair. This can be done as little or as often as you like.

Hair Rinse

Home-made shampoos are alkaline by nature and, in order to restore the acid balance of the hair, an acid rinse should be used after shampooing.

500ml (16fl oz) warm water
1 tablespoon lemon juice or cider vinegar
5 drops essential oil blend

Mix all the ingredients together in a jug. Place a bowl in the washbasin, bend over the basin and pour the rinse over your hair, catching the surplus in the bowl. Empty back into the jug and repeat several times.

Herbal infusions or decoctions can also be added to the rinse for further therapeutic action.

BATHS

Poor Marie Antoinette had to clothe herself in a voluminous flannel nightshirt in order to have a bath as the church at that time had decreed that nudity was wicked. We are fortunate to live in an age where bodies are acknowledged as being okay and the taking of a bath can be fun as well as healing, hydrating, relaxing, beautifying or sensual.

Everyone knows the clean, relaxed feeling after a long, leisurely bath but the benefits can be infinitely more in terms of health. Bathing is an 'anti-stress' aid. Run a deep bath, pour something pleasant into the water (usually an experiment), light a perfumed candle, spread a soothing mask on your face, and lie back against a bath pillow, or a hot-water bottle filled with warm water, sipping a warm drink and listening to soft music. You can slip into that wonderful state of 'being nowhere' and remain there for as long as it takes. Your stress will run down the drain with the bath water and you can leave the bathroom ready to take on the world again.

Skin (which is the largest organ in the body) has been described as the 'third kidney' because of its sweat glands. Like the kidneys, these glands excrete mineral salts, toxins, nitrogenous wastes and water. Given the right conditions, our skins may be responsible for the excretion of one-third of the body's waste products. To do this properly, the pores have to be free of dead cells, dirt and excess oil. If the sweat glands are unable to function properly, an additional load is thrown onto the kidneys.

There are many ways of getting maximum value from your bath such as pre-bath treatments, bath oils, after-bath colognes, powders and oils. You will find recipes for all these in the following pages.

DRY BRUSH MASSAGE

This is a preliminary to the bath. It ensures that all dead skin is removed and the circulation stimulated. You will need a body brush with a long, preferably removable, handle. These are quite inexpensive and can be bought at health food shops or pharmacies. You can use a long loofah but I find a brush easier.

Brush the whole body from the neck down, being gentle on delicate areas such as thighs, abdomen and breasts. Pay particular attention to the areas where there are glands, i.e. the groin, armpits and side of the neck. Brush these areas gently but thoroughly with a circular motion.

SALT RUB

This is another pre-shower or bath method for ridding your skin of the dead cells which make it look sallow and dull. It will stimulate the circulation and leave the skin glowing and clean. Stand in the bath or shower recess to use this rub, as it's pretty messy. It's even better if you share this with a friend and do each other's backs! Don't use the salt scrub on any of the 'tender parts' – they don't like it!

Mix together 1 tablespoon coarse salt and 1 tablespoon Basic Herb Oil of your choice. Add 2 drops essential oil for each tablespoon of the salt mixture.

Lightly oil your body first and then, using a firm circular motion, rub the mixture onto the skin. You will be astonished to see the amount of dirt that comes off. Shower or bathe and use some herbal massage oil to finish. You will feel and look terrific.

FULL BODY BATH

Baths which are too hot or too cold are not relaxing. The temperature should be body heat or very slightly higher. 35–38°C (95–100°F) is about right. However, for a feverish person the water temperature can be up to 45°C (113°F), as long as it feels comfortable to him/her. Never leave a sick person alone in the bath or let him/her spend longer than 5–10 minutes in the bath. Follow the bath by wrapping the patient in blankets to induce sweating. Avoid hot baths at all if you have a heart problem or high blood pressure.

You can buy special pillows for use in the bath, to make yourself as comfortable as possible as you gain most benefit by staying in the water for about 30 minutes.

If you don't want to use oils in the bath, some alternative recipes are given here. These can also be used if you prefer a shower. The bag containing the herbs or oatmeal mixture may be used as a washcloth and, instead of putting infusions in your bath water, you can splash them onto your body after a shower.

Oat Cleanser

This cleanser may be used instead of soap. It makes a good facial scrub by mixing a small amount to a paste with water, gently massaging it into the skin and rinsing off with cool water. When used in the bath, it is very soothing to itchy, sore skin. It's excellent for babies' baths but only the gentlest herbs should be used. Make large quantities of this mixture as it keeps indefinitely if well stored.

1 part powdered bran
2 parts powdered oats
1 part powdered skim milk
3 parts powdered soap (optional)
3 parts powdered herbs

Mix all the ingredients together and store in an airtight jar.

To use, put a cupful of the mixture in a muslin bag (see EQUIPMENT) and tie securely. Put the bag into a saucepan and cover with 8 cups (2 litres/3½ pints) water. Bring nearly to a boil and barely simmer, covered, for 15 minutes. Pour the liquid into the bath and use the muslin bag as a washcloth.

BATH OILS

There are two types of bath oils: floating and dispersible.

FLOATING OILS

I like the floating oil very much because it drifts towards you and settles on your skin where you can gently massage it in. Unfortunately, it doesn't discriminate between your body and the sides of the bath – it drifts that way as well and stays in a ring around the water level. However, cleaning the bath can be a small price to pay for the feeling of silkiness on your skin when you step out of the bath, massage any remaining oil into your skin and blot yourself dry with a soft towel. To use this oil, pour a few tablespoons under the hot water as it's running.

DISPERSIBLE OILS

This oil disappears into the water and doesn't leave a ring around the bath. It needs additives to emulsify the oil to help it to blend with the water.

It's best to make small quantities of these oils until you find the one you like and then make lots. It will keep a long time if stored in a dark cupboard in the bathroom.

Floating Bath Oil

2⅓ cups (580ml/19fl oz) Basic Herb Oil
3 teaspoons essential oil

Mix all the ingredients together, then bottle and shake well.

Semi-dispersible Bath Oil (1)

This is a very luxurious and moisturising bath oil. Add 4–8 teaspoons to the water as the bath is filling.

2 cups (500ml/16fl oz) cold
Triple Strength Infusion
1½ tablespoons glycerine
2 teaspoons tragacanth
⅓ cup (80ml/2½fl oz) **Basic Herb Oil**
2 teaspoons essential oil

Mix the infusion with the glycerine in a jug, then mix very slowly with the tragacanth to make smooth paste.

Add the Basic Herb Oil, stirring to mix well, then add the essential oil slowly, stirring well. Bottle.

Semi-dispersible Bath Oil (2)

Bathing in this oil is a lovely, fragrant, aromatherapeutic experience. You might like to choose one of the cologne mixtures from Colognes Using Essential Oils or make a mixture to deal with a specific problem. Sprinkle one teaspoon only into the filled bath.

½ cup (125ml/4fl oz) vodka,
highest proof possible
2 teaspoons essential oils
1 teaspoon glycerine

Bottle all the ingredients and shake well.

Herbal Semi-dispersible Bath Oil

Add 1–2 tablespoons of the bath oil to the bath. Shake before use.

1 cup (250ml/8fl oz) **Basic Herb Oil**
2 tablespoons coconut shampoo or
other good shampoo
3 teaspoons essential oil

Bottle all the ingredients and shake to combine.

EPSOM SALTS BATH

Epsom salts can help the body to get rid of toxins and are particularly beneficial for easing joint and muscle pain and stiffness. To make the bath add 1 cup (220g/7oz) Epsom salts and the herbs or oils of your choice as the bath is running and make sure the salts are dissolved. Stay in the bath for 20–30 minutes, massaging affected parts of your body while in the bath. Suggestions for using herbs in conjunction with the salts will be found in the Therapeutic Herbal Baths Chart. Essential oils may be substituted for herbs.

FOOT BATH

A foot bath is, as the name suggests, a bath for the feet. Ideally the bath should be deep enough to cover the calves of the legs as well. Foot baths can ease the pain of aching feet, stimulate circulation, ease tension headaches, lessen the symptoms of colds and influenza and relax the nervous system.

The mustard foot bath is the best known and most widely used.

Cold foot baths will soothe tired feet and help to stop nose bleeds.

The herbs in the Therapeutic Herbal Baths Chart may be used either fresh or dried. Instructions for making infusions and decoctions will be found in Herbal Preparation Methods.

Further suggestions for bath treatments will be found in Chapter 5.

Mustard Foot Baths

Dissolve 2 tablespoons dry mustard and add to a foot bath of hot water. Keep your feet immersed for 15–30 minutes, topping up with more hot water as needed.

ESSENTIAL OILS IN BATHS

Essential oils can also be used in the bath to help soothe away ailments. Keep them out of reach of children, as some are toxic if swallowed, even in small quantities. To keep the oils potent for as long as possible, store them in amber glass away from light and heat. These oils add antiseptic qualities to your bath as well as providing a delightful fragrance to help you relax.

Basil

Cinnamon

Clove

Eucalyptus

Lavender

Lemon Grass

Peppermint

Pine

Rosemary

Tea Tree

Thyme

Ylang-ylang

BODY POWDER

If you enjoy using powder after a bath or shower, here is a recipe for a natural one. A word of caution though: powder used excessively can block the pores of the skin.

Basic Body Powder

Arrowroot powder or Cornflour or Talc (available from pharmaceutical suppliers)

Mix one of the above with an equal quantity of powdered dried herbs, citrus peel and spices. You can add a few drops of essential oil (not too much, or the powder will go lumpy). Mix all the ingredients well and rub through a sieve. Store in a flat bowl with a lid and apply with a large wad of cotton wool.

BODY POWDER BLENDS

Always check carefully before choosing herbs for powder (especially for babies) to make sure that the herb will not cause an allergic reaction on the skin. This is especially important with chamomile.

For Babies

Chamomile

Lemon balm

Deodorant

Rosemary

Thyme

Sage

Lavender

Orange peel

For Men

Liquorice

Rosemary

Lavender

Coriander seed

THERAPEUTIC HERBAL BATHS

Baths can have more than just a soothing effect. They can help to remedy a variety of ills as well, as you will see from the chart. Make either a Triple Strength Infusion and pour the strained liquid into the bath, or make it as in the Oat Cleanser recipe but with herbs as the only ingredient. I like the bag method best as I enjoy scrubbing myself with the bagful of herbs.

ARTHRITIS

REMEDY:
Rosemary, thyme, Epsom salts

HOW TO USE:
Make 1 litre ($1^3/_4$ pints) of Triple Strength Infusion of the herbs. Add 1 cup (220g/7oz) of Epsom salts to the infusion, stir to dissolve. Pour into a deep bath which is a little hotter than usual. Remain in the bath for 30 minutes massaging affected parts of the body while in the bath.

CHILLS AND COLDS

REMEDY:
a) Mustard foot bath
b) Borage, sage, thyme

HOW TO USE:
a) Dissolve 2 tablespoons dry mustard and add to a foot bath of hot water. Keep your feet immersed for 15–30 minutes, topping up with more hot water as needed.
b) Make 1 litre ($1^3/_4$ pints) of Triple Strength Infusion and pour into a hot bath. Soak your feet for 15–25 minutes.

CRAMPS, MUSCULAR

REMEDY:
Rosemary, thyme, Epsom salts

HOW TO USE:
Make 1 litre ($1^3/_4$ pints) of Triple Strength Infusion, dissolve the Epsom salts and pour into a hot bath. Soak for 20–25 minutes, massaging the affected limbs.

ECZEMA

REMEDY:
a) Bran, oats
b) Calendula, chickweed, yarrow

HOW TO USE:
a) Mix or use singly. Put 1 cup (about 90g/3oz) in a muslin bag and tie the top securely. Put the bag into a saucepan and cover with 2 litres ($3^1/_3$ pints) water. Bring to the boil and barely simmer, covered, for 15 minutes. Pour the liquid into the bath and use the muslin bag as a washcloth. Don't use soap.
b) Make 1 litre ($1^3/_4$ pints) of Triple Strength Infusion and add to a warm bath making sure that the affected areas are either submerged or sponged repeatedly with the water.

FIBROSITIS

REMEDY:
Epsom salts, thyme.

HOW TO USE:
See ARTHRITIS

HEADACHES

REMEDY:
a) Lavender
b) Mustard

HOW TO USE:
a) Make 1 litre ($1^3/_4$ pints) Triple Strength Infusion. Add to a warm bath. Add 10 drops lavender essential oil, swirl to distribute. Relax for 20 minutes (see also Essential Oils in this chapter).
b) See CHILLS AND COLDS.

INFLUENZA

See CHILLS AND COLDS and also HEALTHY REMEDIES CHART

INSOMNIA

See also HEALTHY REMEDIES CHART

REMEDY:
Chamomile, lavender, lemon balm

HOW TO USE:
Make 1 litre ($1^3/4$ pints) Triple Strength Infusion, pour into a warm bath. Relax for 20 minutes while sipping a cup of chamomile infusion.

LUMBAGO

See ARTHRITIS

MUSCLES, SORE

REMEDY:
Rosemary, sage, thyme, Epsom salts

HOW TO USE:
Make 1 litre ($1^3/4$ pints) Triple Strength Infusion, add the Epsom salts and dissolve. Pour into a hot bath. Soak for 20–30 minutes, massaging the sore muscles. Follow with massage (see ESSENTIAL OIL REMEDIES).

NERVOUS EXHAUSTION AND STRESS

REMEDY:
Chamomile, lemon balm, thyme, valerian

HOW TO USE:
Make a Triple Strength Infusion and pour into a warm bath. Soak for 20–30 minutes while sipping a cup of chamomile infusion.

POOR CIRCULATION

REMEDY:
a) Mustard
b) Nettle, pennyroyal, sage

HOW TO USE:
a) Mustard footbath see CHILLS AND COLDS.
b) Make 1 litre ($1^3/4$ pints) Triple Strength Infusion and pour into a hot bath. Soak for 15–20 minutes.

PSORIASIS

See also HEALTHY REMEDIES CHART
REMEDY:
a) Bran and oats
b) Lavender, thyme, yarrow

HOW TO USE:
a) See ECZEMA
b) Make 1 litre ($1^3/4$ pints) Triple Strength Infusion. Soak in a warm bath for 15 minutes bathing affected parts. Use the infusion as a compress on affected parts between baths.

SKIN, DRY AND/OR ITCHY

REMEDY:
a) Comfrey root, mallow root, 2 cups (200g/7oz) dried milk
b) Bran and oats

HOW TO USE:
a) Make 1 litre ($1^3/4$ pints) decoction using the herb roots. Mix the dried milk into the decoction and pour into a warm bath. Soak for 10 minutes.
b) See ECZEMA. Use the bag in place of soap for its cleansing, soothing and non-drying action.

CHAPTER FIVE

AROMA-THERAPY AND HERBS

I was in my garden very early this morning

enjoying the warm, newly-risen sun and the fresh, still air.

As I stood there, a sly wind came around the corner of the

house, the plants shivered, and I was overwhelmed with the

perfumes of rosemary, lavender, jasmine, rose geranium and a

host of other scents blending to create a heady potpourri more

wonderful than I could ever invent in my workshop.

This chapter leads you into the world of essential oils; a

beguiling world from which you, like me, may

never want to escape.

Most of the great civilisations of the world have used plants and their essences. Chinese, Greek, Egyptian and Indian records date back in some instances to 2000 BC. The plants and essences were not used merely for the aroma but for religious and purification ceremonies, healing, embalming, preserving, fumigation, the making of aphrodisiac oils and love potions, and oils and creams to beautify the body and hair. The Arabian physician Avicenna (980–1037) is credited with the discovery of the distillation of essential oils from plants. These first oils must have been more precious than gold and indeed the oils have been fairly rare until comparatively recently. We are fortunate that today we are able to buy the finest oils available on this planet: rose from Bulgaria, neroli from Italy, sandalwood from India, tea tree from Australia and peppermint from England, just to name a few.

The essential oils are found in miniscule amounts in most plants which is why the finished oils are seemingly expensive. If you consider the power of the oils and how few drops are used, the cost of the oils becomes less alarming and more understandable. Many supermarkets and variety stores now carry ranges of potpourris and diffusers next to which is normally a display of 'oils'. These are usually labelled as fragrant oil, compounded oil or perfume oil; they are synthetic, cheap and of no therapeutic value at all. Buy your oils from a reputable source and make sure that they are labelled 100% pure essential oil. Oils such as rose, neroli, chamomile and many more are so expensive that it puts them beyond the reach of most pockets. To overcome this problem many of the oil companies are now offering bottles of 2–3% essential oil in almond (or similar) oil. This means that we can all have these rare and special oils in our collection.

Once your nose has become accustomed to the smell of the real thing it will be deeply offended when assaulted by synthetic perfumes.

The essential oils are found in leaves (such as eucalyptus), petals (rose), bark (sandalwood), resins (myrrh), roots (calamus), rind (citrus fruits) and seeds (caraway). The term 'essential oils' causes some confusion as people tend to think of these essences as being the same as the more familiar olive, canola, safflower and other 'fixed' oils. Essential oils are non-oily and, unlike the fixed oils, they evaporate when exposed to air.

Take care of the oils by storing them in amber glass bottles, in a box, in a dark, cool cupboard.

Essential oils can't always be used in the same way as the herb from which they were extracted. This is partly due to the strength and also to the fact that some of the constituents of the plant may be missing from the essential oil. Don't assume that the oils can be substituted for the herb, and always follow instructions regarding quantities and safety data.

The molecules of essential oils are so small that they are readily absorbed into the skin or lungs and from there enter the bloodstream and are carried around the body to exert their power over bodily organs and systems. There is a theory that not only is it safer to use the oils externally or for inhalation but that they work better, as the stomach and its acids are bypassed. Take the oils internally only on the advice of a professional.

Use the oils in the following ways taking care to only use in the amounts suggested:
- massage oils
- fomentations and compresses
- baths
- toilet waters and perfumes
- insect repellents
- cosmetic creams, lotions and healing creams
- shampoos, conditioners and hair tonics
- potpourris and sachets
- room-freshener sprays
- preparations for pets, to help heal skin conditions and repel fleas
- floor and furniture cleaners
- kitchen, laundry and toilet sweeteners and cleansers

Cautions:
All essential oils should be kept well out of the reach of children as most are lethal if drunk, even in small quantities.

Some of the essences are very toxic and should be used internally only on the advice of a qualified therapist.

Essential oils should mostly be combined with a carrier (base) oil, such as olive or sweet almond oil, before using externally as they are too strong to use alone. The total amount of all essential oils used in a blend (either singly or combined with other ingredients) should never exceed 3% of the mixture, including the carrier oil, and some oils should be used in far smaller amounts.

It's imperative to use only the best essential oils available. Synthetics and compounded oils don't have the healing properties of the real thing and could be dangerous if taken internally. Many oils are labelled as fragrant oil, compounded oil, or perfume oil. These descriptions mean that the oil is synthetic or blended with either paraffin oil or a carrier oil. Check with the retailer that oil labelled '100% pure, natural, essential oil' is in fact just that. If in doubt, wait until you find a reliable source. Another check is cost. If oils such as rose, jasmine or neroli (to mention but a few) are roughly the same price as the more common lavender, rosemary and peppermint, then they are almost certainly not the real thing.

METHODS OF EXTRACTION

DISTILLATION

The most widely used commercial method of extracting essential oil is by distillation, where steam or boiling water is used to evaporate the oil which then passes in coils through a container of cold water. A further container separates the water from the oil.

SOLVENT EXTRACTION

The perfume industry sometimes uses a spirit solvent, often petroleum ether, to dissolve the oil in the plant. The solvent is evaporated off, leaving a hard, heavily perfumed natural wax substance called a concrete. The wax is then separated from the essence and the resulting liquid is called an absolute, the most concentrated perfume available. This method produces a purer perfume than distillation but is more expensive and impractical to do at home.

ENFLEURAGE

A time-honoured method of recovering essential oil from petals which retain their perfume for some time after collection (such as tuberose, rose and jasmine) is called enfleurage. This art is dying as the cost of skilled labour becomes prohibitive for commercial oil producers.

MACERATION

Perfumed petals are placed into a jar one-quarter filled with cotton wool balls and sweet almond oil. The jar is tightly covered and left for two days in a warm spot. The petals are then replaced with fresh ones. This is repeated for up to a month.

The method is very simple, but a steady, very gentle source of heat is essential. I put the jar on top of the refrigerator, towards the back where the rising heat from the coils remains gentle and constant. An airing cupboard or similar source of constant heat is also acceptable.

EXPRESSION

The oil in citrus plants is contained in glands in the outer skin. In earlier times, the skins of the citrus were squeezed by hand until the glands burst, the droplets being collected in sponges which were then squeezed to collect the oil in containers. Now the process is by machine.

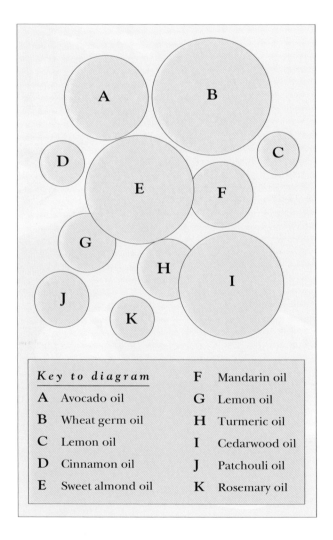

Key to diagram		
	F	Mandarin oil
A Avocado oil	G	Lemon oil
B Wheat germ oil	H	Turmeric oil
C Lemon oil	I	Cedarwood oil
D Cinnamon oil	J	Patchouli oil
E Sweet almond oil	K	Rosemary oil

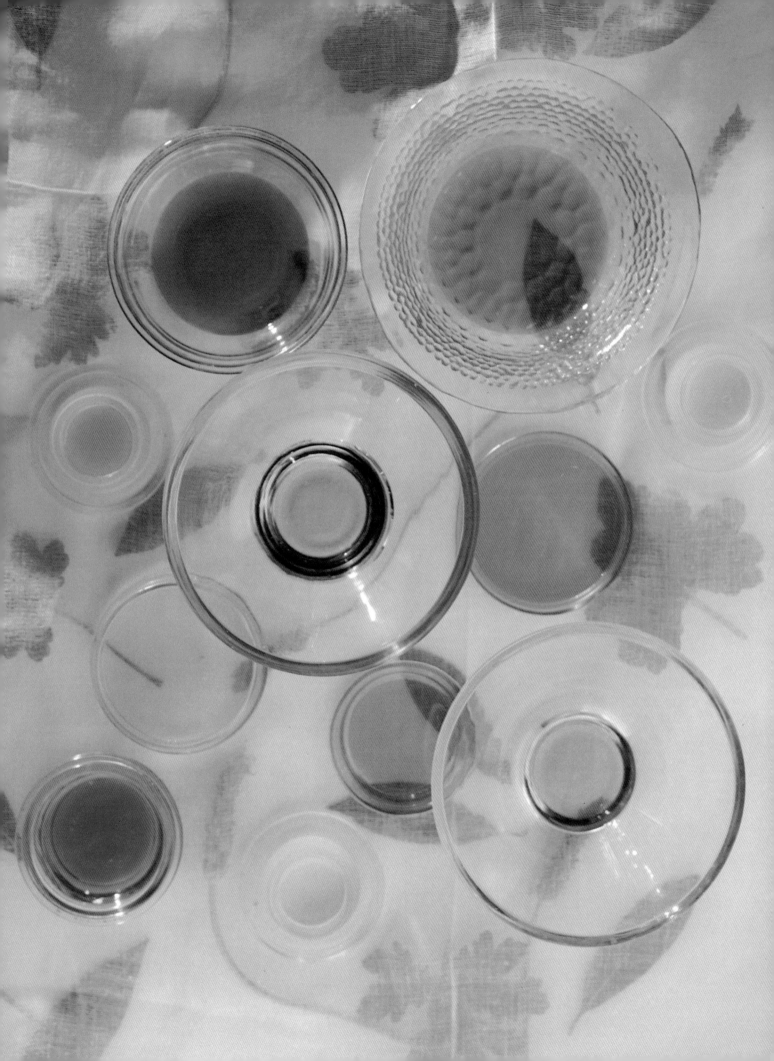

BLENDING GUIDE

The following list gives a general idea of the amounts to use. Individual recipes may specify more or less.

Massage oils	2%–2.5%
Face oils	1%–1.5%
Fomentations and compresses	10 drops to 100ml (3^{1}/$_{3}$fl oz)
Ointments	3%
Creams and lotions	1%–1.5%
Baths	10 drops maximum. Swish the water well to disperse, or add the essential oil to 1 tablespoon of olive oil, vodka or full-cream milk and pour into the bath. Swish well.
Toilet waters/perfumes	Varies. See pertinent recipes.
Insect repellent rubs	2%–2.5%
Room sprays, all types	1 teaspoon in 50ml (1^{2}/$_{3}$fl oz) alcohol. Dissolve and then add 250ml (8fl oz) purified water.
Shampoos and conditioners	1%–1.5%
Potpourris	Varies. See pertinent recipes.
Pet shampoo	1 drop in shampoo; 1 more in rinsing water.
Floor and furniture cleaners	2% or whatever smells good!

BLENDING CHART

In any sized bottle the main content will be a carrier such as oil, vinegar or alcohol in which to dilute the essential oils. (A 'carrier oil' is also known as a 'base oil'.) The following chart gives the amounts of essential oils to add in order to achieve 1%, 2% or 3% dilution.

100ml (3^{1}/$_{3}$fl oz) bottle
18–20 drops = 1ml in 100ml (3^{1}/$_{3}$fl oz) bottle = approx 1%
30–40 drops = 2ml in 100ml (3^{1}/$_{3}$fl oz) bottle = approx 2%
54–60 drops = 3ml in 100ml (3^{1}/$_{3}$fl oz) bottle = approx 3%

50ml (1^{2}/$_{3}$fl oz) bottle
9–10 drops = 0.5ml in 50ml (1^{2}/$_{3}$fl oz) bottle = approx 1%
18–20 drops = 1ml in 50ml (1^{2}/$_{3}$fl oz) bottle = approx 2%
27–30 drops = 1.5ml in 50ml (1^{2}/$_{3}$fl oz) bottle = approx 3%

10ml (^{1}/$_{3}$fl oz) bottle
2 drops in 10ml (^{1}/$_{3}$fl oz) bottle = approx 1%
4 drops in 10ml (^{1}/$_{3}$fl oz) bottle = approx 2%
6 drops in 10ml (^{1}/$_{3}$fl oz) bottle = approx 3%

BLENDING AND DILUTING THE OILS

For ease of measuring and for safety's sake, I would strongly advise you to buy some accurate measurers. A set of metric measuring spoons is more accurate than regular household spoons, but they are still not as good as those made to pharmaceutical/laboratory standards.

18–20 drops = 1ml = 1 marked dropper
90–100 drops = 5ml = 1 metric teaspoon
20ml = 1 metric tablespoon

PROPORTIONS FOR BLENDS

BASE OILS TO ACT AS A CARRIER
86% almond oil, olive oil, grapeseed oil, Basic Herb Oil or other fixed oil suitable for your skin type (see Oils for Skin)
5% avocado oil: helps absorption of other oils and is highly nourishing
5% wheat germ oil: preservative, nutrient and emollient
2% evening primrose oil: nutrient and emollient

ADD
2% essential oils, chosen from those suitable for your skin type

TOTAL
100%

If you don't want to make 100ml ($3^{1}/_{3}$fl oz) you can use the above percentage example to make 50ml ($1^{2}/_{3}$fl oz) or less. Most of the following recipes are worked out on the above examples of 100ml ($3^{1}/_{3}$fl oz).

If you don't have oils such as evening primrose, jojoba or carrot it doesn't matter. It's perfectly all right to use more of the main oil, such as olive or almond, but do try to afford some wheat germ oil (not expensive) and include 5%–10% to act as a preservative.

ABC OF ESSENTIAL OILS

The following essential oils are the ones most widely used (I have marked my personal favourites with an asterisk). They have the widest applications and fortunately many of them are the least expensive. The applications suggested for the oils are all external or for inhalations, mouthwashes and gargles. Internal use is advisable only on the advice of an aromatherapist or other health professional.

See BLENDING AND DILUTING THE OILS for instructions. Never use the undiluted oils directly on the skin.

BASIL
Ocimum basilicum

PARTS USED: Flowering tops and leaves

MAIN USES: Antiseptic, muscle sprain, rheumatism, flatulence, uterine cramps, fever, infectious diseases, bronchitis and migraine. Depression, hysteria, insomnia, mental fatigue and anxiety. Soaps, cosmetics and perfumes.

BLENDS WITH: Bergamot, black pepper, clary sage, lime, geranium, hyssop, lavender, sandalwood.

Caution:
Avoid during pregnancy. Never take internally.

Basil

BENZOIN*
Styrax benzoin

PARTS USED: Gum from trunk of tree

MAIN USES: Tissue inflammation, rheumatism, arthritis, antiseptic treatment for wounds, bronchitis, coughs and influenza. Nervous tension and emotional 'burn-out'. Cosmetically it may be used as an antioxidant to help preserve oils, as a fixative in perfumes and an additive to cosmetics, soaps and perfumes.

BLENDS WITH: Bergamot, cypress, frankincense, juniper, myrrh, sandalwood.

Caution:
Only simple tincture of benzoin should be used.

BERGAMOT*
Citrus bergamia

PARTS USED: Peel of fruit

MAIN USES: Cystitis and thrush, colds and flu and assists in avoiding infectious diseases. Cosmetically used in oily skin, acne, psoriasis and scabies preparations, as a fixative in perfumery, and is a major ingredient in traditional Eau de Cologne.

BLENDS WITH: Chamomile, cypress, lavender, geranium, lemon, juniper, ylang-ylang.

Caution:
Will cause pigmentation if used on skin which is exposed to the sun.

BLACK PEPPER
Piper nigrum

PARTS USED: Dried, unripe fruit

MAIN USES: Rheumatism, arthritis, neuralgia, muscle sprains, stiff joints and to dispel bruises. Anaemia. Add to massage oils for pre-sport application on joints and muscles. Digestive problems, colic, constipation and nausea. Boosts immune system function and expels toxins. Use in baths, inhalations and massage oils to strengthen the nervous system and brain.

BLENDS WITH: Lavender, frankincense, rosemary, sandalwood.

CEDARWOOD
Juniperus virginiana

PARTS USED: Wood

MAIN USES: Acne, skin diseases, antiseptic wash, insect repellent, osteoarthritis, rheumatism, bronchitis and catarrh. Insomnia and depression. Perfume fixative.

BLENDS WITH: Benzoin, cypress, jasmine, juniper, lemon, rose, rosemary, sandalwood.

Caution:
Not to be used internally. Not to be used at all during pregnancy. An irritant to some sensitive skins.

CHAMOMILE *
Anthemis nobilis,
Matricaria chamomilla

PARTS USED: Flowers
MAIN USES: Flatulence, diarrhoea and stomach cramps, irregular and painful periods, anorexia, anti-inflammatory and antiseptic, skin treatments. Soothes mental pain and stress, depression and insomnia. Cosmetically it may be included in preparations for fair hair, dry, itchy skin, puffiness and most skin complaints.
BLENDS WITH: Benzoin, bergamot, clary sage, geranium, jasmine, lavender, neroli, rose, ylang-ylang.

CLARY SAGE *
Salvia sclarea

Use in preference to Sage (*Salvia officinalis*)
PARTS USED: Flowering tops and leaves.
MAIN USES: Menstrual pain, cramps and irregularity, during labour to ease and encourage contractions, controls excessive perspiration, reduces inflammation. Strengthens the autoimmune system. Use cosmetically in creams and lotions for its cell regenerating properties. Use in

Caution:
Never use in pregnancy until labour has started. Avoid large doses – can cause headache and euphoria.

shampoos and rinses to help to control dandruff and greasy hair.
BLENDS WITH: Bergamot and other citrus oils, cedarwood, cypress, frankincense, lavender, pine, sandalwood.

CLOVE *
Eugenia carophyllus

PARTS USED: Buds, leaves and stems
MAIN USES: Analgesic to ease toothache, arthritis and rheumatism. Skin infections and ulcers (see caution below). Increases resistance to bacteria. Use in small amounts in perfumes as a fixative.
BLENDS WITH: Basil, benzoin, bergamot and all citrus oils, rose, peppermint, yang-ylang.

Caution:
Must never be used neat or in high concentrations on skin as it could cause severe irritation.

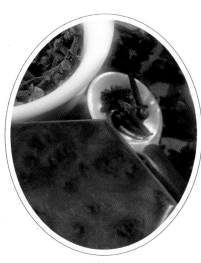

Clove

CYPRESS
Cupressus sempervirens

PARTS USED: Twigs, needles and cones
MAIN USES: Menopausal problems, circulatory stimulant for cold hands, feet and varicose veins. Coughs, colds, laryngitis. Calms the excitable, eases grief. Cosmetically useful in lotions for oily skins, dehydrated skins and broken capillaries.
BLENDS WITH: Cedarwood, juniper, lavender, mandarin, marjoram, pine, sandalwood.

Caution:
Probably best to avoid during pregnancy.

EUCALYPTUS *
Eucalyptus globulus

PARTS USED: Leaves and young twigs
MAIN USES: Antiviral, antibacterial treatment for coughs, catarrh, influenza, sinusitis, infectious diseases, wounds and fevers. Eases muscular aches and pains. Flea repellent.
BLENDS WITH: Benzoin, juniper, lavender, lemon, lemon grass, pine, thyme.

FENNEL
Foeniculum vulgare

PARTS USED: Seeds

MAIN USES: Menopausal irregularities, helps to rid the body of toxins, helps to disperse obesity, cellulite and fluid retention. Liver cleanser and anti-inflammatory. Use in cosmetic lotions and creams as a tonic and cleanser.

BLENDS WITH: Basil, geranium, lavender, lemon, rose, rosemary, sandalwood.

> **Caution:**
> Phototoxic. Not to be used on the skin before exposure to sunlight. Not to be used internally. Not to be used by epileptics or during pregnancy.

Fennel

FRANKINCENSE
Boswellia thurifera
B carterii

PARTS USED: Bark

MAIN USES: Urinary/genital tract infections. Asthma, catarrh and general respiratory conditions. Soothes and calms during and after labour. Calms soothes and comforts the mind. Stimulates ageing skin and helps to keep wrinkles at bay.

BLENDS WITH: Basil, bergamot, black pepper, lavender, orange, patchouli, pine, sandalwood.

> **Caution:**
> Can be irritating if used directly on the skin.

GERANIUM*
Pelargonium graveolens

PARTS USED: Flowers and leaves

MAIN USES: Hormonal system, helps to remove toxins from the liver and kidneys and to stimulate the autoimmune system. Throat and mouth infections. Stress and depression, particularly that of menopause. Cosmetically improves circulation to the skin, balances the sebum in oily, sluggish skin. Dermatitis and eczema.

BLENDS WITH: Basil, bergamot, lavender, patchouli, rose, rosemary, sandalwood.

GINGER
Zingiber officinalis

PARTS USED: Root

MAIN USES: Improves circulation, eases arthritic and rheumatic pain, cramps, sprains and muscle spasms. Loss of appetite, flatulence, diarrhoea, sore throats, tonsillitis and catarrh, nausea and motion sickness. Restores energy and lifts the spirit.

BLENDS WITH: Citrus oils, cedar-wood, clove, frankincense, rose, spearmint.

GRAPEFRUIT
Citrus paradisi

PARTS USED: Peel

MAIN USES: Lymphatic stimulant, cellulitis, obesity, chills, colds, flu, nervous exhaustion, migraine and premenstrual syndrome. Acne and oily skin.

BLENDS WITH: Basil, chamomile, other citrus oils, cypress, lavender, geranium, rose, ylang-ylang.

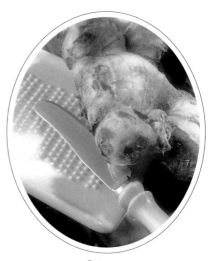

Ginger

JASMINE
Jasminum officinale,
J. grandiflorum

PARTS USED: Flowers
MAIN USES: Eases the pain of menstruation and labour, useful for coughs, catarrh, hoarseness and laryngitis. Reputed to increase the number of spermatozoa. Use to ease depression and listlessness. Cosmetically used for dry and sensitive skin but will benefit all skins.
BLENDS WITH: Everything!

JUNIPER
Juniperus communis

PARTS USED: Berries
MAIN USES: Gout. An antiseptic for the genitourinary system. Digestive, antitoxin. Colds and flu. Acne, dermatitis and eczema.
BLENDS WITH: Cedarwood, all citrus, cypress, lavender, pine, sandalwood.

Caution:
Not to be used during pregnancy or by those with severe kidney disease.

LAVENDER*
Lavandula officinalis

PARTS USED: Flowers
MAIN USES: Antiseptic, antibacterial, stimulates cell growth, eases muscular spasm, sprains, rheumatism. Rectifies menstrual irregularity, scantiness and pain. Eases and helps to heal minor burns and scalds, hastens the healing of abscesses, boils and carbuncles. Insect repellent.
BLENDS WITH: Most other oils.

Lavender

LEMON*
Citrus limonum

PARTS USED: Peel
MAIN USES: Digestive, liver and gall bladder problems. Water purifier. Lymphatic toner. Antiseptic, sore throats, coughs, colds and flu. Reduces fever. Digestive, antacid. Heart tonic. Stimulates the immune system. Acne, insect bites and warts. Anaemia.
BLENDS WITH: Benzoin, chamomile, eucalyptus, juniper, lavender, other citrus oils, sandalwood, ylang-ylang.

MANDARIN
Citrus madurensis

PARTS USED: Peel
MAIN USES: Digestion, flatulence, appetite stimulant. Tonic for liver and gall bladder. Mild, strengthening and gentle for children, menopausal and pregnant women.
BLENDS WITH: Black pepper, chamomile, lavender, marjoram, other citrus oils, rose.

Lemon

MARJORAM
Origanum marjorana

PARTS USED: Flowering tops and leaves

MAIN USES: Analgesic for bruises, sprains, lower back, rheumatism, joint and muscle pain. Heart tonic, may lower blood pressure. Eases stomach cramps, indigestion and flatulence. Colds, headache and migraine.

BLENDS WITH: Bergamot, cedarwood, chamomile, lavender, mandarin, rosemary, ylang-ylang.

Caution:
Avoid prolonged use. Never use during pregnancy.

MELISSA (LEMON BALM)*
Melissa officinalis

PARTS USED: Leaves and flowers

MAIN USES: Indigestion and nausea, Tonic to the cardiovascular and reproductive systems. Antiseptic, antiviral and antifungal. Acne, eczema, bee stings. Shock, hysteria, grief.

BLENDS WITH: Chamomile, frankincense, geranium, lavender, petitgrain, ylang-ylang.

MINT, PEPPER*
Mentha piperita

PARTS USED: Leaves

MAIN USES: Indigestion, flatulence, diarrhoea, nausea and vomiting. Anaemia. Antispasmodic useful for stomach cramps, asthma, coughs and bronchitis. Eases neuralgia and rheumatic pain. Shock, hysteria and palpitations. Insect repellent. Dermatitis, ringworm, scabies, itching, inflammation and sunburn.

BLENDS WITH: Benzoin, cedarwood, cypress, lavender, mandarin, marjoram, pine, rosemary, spearmint.

Caution:
Use only 0.5-1%. Avoid during pregnancy.

Melissa

MINT, SPEAR*
Mentha spicata

PARTS USED: Flowering tops and leaves

MAIN USES: To be preferred to peppermint for children. Asthma, bronchitis and sinusitis. Digestive system, flatulence, vomiting, nausea, constipation, diarrhoea, travel nausea and sickness. Colds, fever and flu. Headache, migraine and nervous stress.

BLENDS WITH: Basil, grapefruit, peppermint, rosemary.

MYRRH*
Commiphora myrrha

PARTS USED: Bark, resin

MAIN USES: Antiseptic, fungicidal, mouthwash for mouth ulcers, gingivitis, pyorrhoea, spongy gums. Oral and vaginal thrush. Anti-inflammatory. Eases grief and loss. Eczema, athletes foot and tinea.

BLENDS WITH: Benzoin, frankincense, lavender, patchouli.

NEROLI
(Orange blossom)
Citrus vulgaris

PARTS USED: Petals

MAIN USES: Digestive, flatulence, colitis and diarrhoea related to shock. Neuralgia and headaches. Tranquilliser for insomnia, premenstrual syndrome, depression, nerves and anxiety. Improves skin elasticity in dry, mature skins, scarring, thread veins and stretch marks.

BLENDS WITH: Most other oils.

ORANGE
Citrus vulgaris

PARTS USED: Peel

MAIN USES: Antiseptic. Obesity and water retention. Lymphatic tonic. Colds and bronchitis. Reduces fever. Constipation and indigestion. Tension and stress. Dry skin and wrinkles.

BLENDS WITH: Benzoin, clove, frankincense, jasmine, juniper, lavender, neroli, rose.

> **Caution:**
> May cause irritation to those with sensitive skin.

PATCHOULI*
Pogostemon cablin

PARTS USED: Leaves

MAIN USES: Fungicidal, antiseptic, antibacterial. Acne, athlete's foot, dermatitis, eczema, fungal infections and impetigo. Insect repellent. Wounds and wrinkles. An excellent fixative for perfumes.

BLENDS WITH: In small amounts blends well with most other oils.

PETITGRAIN*
Citrus aurantium

PARTS USED: Leaves and young twigs

MAIN USES: Acne, pimples and greasy hair. Anxiety, insomnia, brightens and cheers the mind. Deodorising and a valuable addition to perfumes.

BLENDS WITH: Most other oils.

Orange

PINE*
Pinus sylvestris

PARTS USED: Needles, twigs and cones

MAIN USES: Powerful antiseptic. Asthma, bronchitis, catarrh, colds, flu, coughs, sinusitis and sore throat. Cystitis and hepatitis. Arthritis, rheumatism, gout and neuralgia.

BLENDS WITH: Cedarwood, eucalyptus, lavender, rosemary, sage, tea tree.

ROSE
Rosa centifolia, R. damascena, R. gallica

PARTS USED: Petals

MAIN USES: Menstrual irregularities, leucorrhoea, premenstrual syndrome and reputed to increase sperm. Palpitations and poor circulation. Stimulates secretion of bile. Nausea and vomiting. Asthma, coughs and hay fever. Depression and nervous tension. Good for all skins, tonic and soothing.

BLENDS WITH: Most other oils.

ROSEMARY*
Rosmarinus officinalis

PARTS USED: Leaves
MAIN USES: Powerful antiseptic, antibacterial, astringent, antispasmodic and analgesic. Asthma, coughs, colds, flu and bronchitis. Headache and neuralgia. Gout and rheumatism. Liver and gall bladder. Wounds and burns. Indigestion, flatulence, constipation and diarrhoea. Dandruff and hair growth.
BLENDS WITH: Basil, citrus oils, frankincense, geranium, lavender, peppermint, petitgrain.

> **Caution:**
> Not to be used during pregnancy or by those with high blood pressure or epilepsy.

Rosemary

SANDALWOOD*
Santalum album

PARTS USED: 25-year-old heartwood
MAIN USES: Antiseptic, urinary system cleanser and cystitis. Antispasmodic, respiratory infections, catarrh, coughs and sore throat. Digestive, colic and nausea. Good for all skins. Eczema, acne, dermatitis, inflammation.
BLENDS WITH: Most, but particularly benzoin, rose, neroli, petitgrain.

TEA TREE*
Melaleuca alternifolia

PARTS USED: Leaves
MAIN USES: Reputed to be 100 times stronger than carbolic acid with the advantage of being safe to use. Disinfectant, antiviral, antifungal, antibacterial and antiseptic. Urinary tract infections, vaginal trichomonas, candida, thrush and herpes. Abscesses, athlete's foot, corns, warts and ringworm. Respiratory infections, coughs, colds, bronchitis, cold sores, mouth ulcers, gingivitis, bad breath and tonsillitis. Acne, boils, minor burns and sunburn.
BLENDS WITH: Clary sage, clove, cypress, eucalyptus, geranium, lavender, lemon, rosemary, thyme.

THYME*
Thymus vulgaris and chemotype 'linalol'

'Linalol' type contains less amount of toxic phenols and in consequence is less of an irritant for skin and safer for children.
PARTS USED: Flowers and leaves
MAIN USES: The most antiseptic essential oil. Antispasmodic. Stimulates the immune system. Respiratory tract, asthma, bronchitis, catarrh, croup, emphysema and whooping cough. Skin, boils, wounds, sores, cold sores, thrush and leucorrhoea. Stimulating, low blood pressure. Digestive, flatulence. Head colds, flu, headaches and sinusitis. Diuretic – removes uric acid in arthritis and gout. Deodorant. Strengthens the nervous system.
BLENDS WITH: Bergamot, cedarwood, juniper, petitgrain, rosemary.

> **Caution:**
> A very powerful oil. Use only 0.5–1%. Never use neat. Never use during pregnancy.

YLANG-YLANG*
Cananga odorata

PARTS USED: Flowers
MAIN USES: High blood pressure and palpitations. Aphrodisiac. Hormone balancer. Reproductive system tonic. Skin care, acne, hair treatments and, perfumes.
BLENDS WITH: Bergamot, jasmine, neroli, patchouli, rose, sandalwood.

ESSENTIAL OIL REMEDIES

Essential oils are highly concentrated and a few are very toxic. In view of this, the oils are usually best employed externally or as inhalations. The oils are readily absorbed through the skin and are then carried around the body via the blood and lymphatic systems to influence internal organs. Because of this ready absorption, an external application is almost always as efficient (sometimes more so) as taking the oils by mouth. The following is an indication of how much oil to use in any treatment. Individual recipes may deviate from these suggestions.

AIR SPRAY: 1 teaspoon in 50ml ($1^2/_3$fl oz) alcohol and 250ml (8fl oz) water.

BATHS: 4–10 drops essential oil (depending on age) in a full bath after the bath has been run.

FOMENTATIONS AND COMPRESSES: 5–10 drops essential oil (depending on age) in 100ml ($3^1/_3$fl oz) water.

GARGLE: 1 drop essential oil in 250ml (8fl oz) water. Mix well. Gargle, spit gargle out. Don't swallow.

INHALATIONS: 5–10 drops essential oil (depending on age) on 2–3 litres ($3^1/_2$–5 pints) hot water.

MASSAGE OILS: 10–20 drops essential oil (depending on age) in 50ml ($1^2/_3$fl oz) carrier oil.

MOUTHWASH: 4 drops in 25ml (about 1fl oz) brandy. To use add 1 teaspoonful to $^1/_4$ cup (60ml/2fl oz) warm water. Rinse mouth thoroughly. Don't swallow.

OINTMENTS: 30 drops essential oil to each 50g ($1^2/_3$oz) jar (this may vary with individual recipes).

WOUND WASH: 10–30 drops essential oil (depending on age) on 100ml ($3^1/_3$fl oz) warm boiled water. Agitate to disperse.

Note:
Wherever possible use a blend of all the recommended oils.

ABRASIONS

ESSENTIAL OILS: Tea tree, lavender
TREATMENT: Wound wash using single or mixed oils. Repeat 2 hourly. Leave uncovered if possible. If a plaster is needed use one drop of either of the oils on the plaster.

ACHES AND PAINS

ESSENTIAL OILS: Marjoram, black pepper, rosemary
TREATMENT: Use a mixture or singly for massage and in a bath.

ANAEMIA

ESSENTIAL OILS: Black pepper, lemon, peppermint
TREATMENT: Use singly or in combination for massage and in a bath.

ARTHRITIS

Osteoarthritis
ESSENTIAL OILS: Cedarwood, black pepper, rosemary
TREATMENT: Use singly or (much better) in combination for massage and in a bath.

Rheumatoid Arthritis
ESSENTIAL OILS: Rosemary, juniper, ginger

ATHLETE'S FOOT

ESSENTIAL OILS: Tea tree, myrrh, thyme
TREATMENT: a) Foot bath using 1 drop of each oil in a bowl (big enough for both feet) containing warm water.
b) Add 2 drops of each oil to 1 teaspoon vegetable oil. Massage the whole foot and between the toes four times a day.
c) Add 2 drops of each oil to 1 cup (150g/5oz) unperfumed talcum powder. Dust the feet before wearing shoes and socks.
d) Pre-soak socks in water to which 10 drops of one of the above oils has been added. Wash them separately from the family laundry.

BITES AND STINGS

Bees
ESSENTIAL OILS: Chamomile, lavender
TREATMENT: Scrape the sting out sideways. Don't pull it out. Mix 1 drop chamomile, 1 drop lavender with 1 teaspoon bicarbonate of soda (counteracts the acidity of the sting) and enough water to make a soft paste. Apply to the painful area. Repeat hourly.

Dogs
ESSENTIAL OILS: Thyme, lavender, tea tree
TREATMENT: Wash the area immediately with a wound wash using the above oils. Apply neat tea tree to the wound, cover with a light dressing. Go straight to hospital if the skin is broken as you may need a tetanus injection.

Insects (Mosquitoes, Gnats or Flies)
ESSENTIAL OILS: Lavender
TREATMENT: Apply neat oil directly on the bite until relief is obtained.

Snakes
ESSENTIAL OILS: Lavender
TREATMENT: Try to identify the snake. Flood wound with lavender oil. Bind limb firmly but not tightly with anything available. Keep patient calm and still. Seek medical help immediately.

Spiders
ESSENTIAL OILS: Lavender
TREATMENT: Try to identify the spider. If you suspect that the spider was of the poisonous variety, go straight to hospital, dabbing the bite constantly with neat lavender oil until hospital treatment begins. If the spider is of a non-poisonous variety treat the bite with 5 drops lavender oil in 1 teaspoon vinegar. Dab on the bite every 4 hours.

Wasps
ESSENTIAL OILS: Lavender
TREATMENT: Add 4 drops lavender oil to 1 teaspoon vinegar. Dab on the wound to counteract the alkaline poison of the sting and reduce pain and swelling. Repeat hourly.

BLEEDING, EXTERNAL

ESSENTIAL OILS: Geranium, lemon, cypress
TREATMENT: Apply a compress containing any or all of the above oils. Bandage firmly but not too tightly in place.

BLISTERS

ESSENTIAL OILS: Lavender, tea tree
TREATMENT: Apply 2 drops of either of the above oils neat. Massage in gently. Don't break the blister.

BOILS AND CARBUNCLES

ESSENTIAL OILS: Bergamot, lavender, tea tree
TREATMENT: Wash the affected area and the surrounding skin 3 times daily by dipping cotton wool balls into a lotion made from 2 drops bergamot oil and 2 drops lavender oil in 50ml (1²/₃fl oz) warm, boiled water. Dispose of the cotton wool balls down the toilet after use. Add 5 drops tea tree oil to 1 teaspoon vegetable oil and smooth on after the wash. Wash the hands well after finishing the treatment. Add 10 drops of tea tree oil to water to soak clothing which has been in contact with the infected area. Wash separately.

BREATH, BAD

ESSENTIAL OILS: Bergamot, peppermint, myrrh
TREATMENT: Make a mouthwash using the above oils. Use as often as needed.

BRONCHITIS

ESSENTIAL OILS: Benzoin, marjoram, eucalyptus
TREATMENT: Inhalation using a blend of the above oils. Gently massage the chest with a blend of the above oils.

BRUISES

ESSENTIAL OILS:
Geranium, clary sage, rosemary
TREATMENT: Hold a bag of frozen peas or iceblocks wrapped in cloth on the area for a few minutes. Massage with a blend of 6 drops total of the above oils in 1 tablespoon vegetable oil.

BURNS AND SCALDS, MINOR

See HEALTHY REMEDIES CHART for a description of minor burns.
ESSENTIAL OILS: Lavender

TREATMENT: Run cold water over the affected area for 10 minutes. If this isn't possible use cold water compresses for 10 minutes, changing very often. Gently pat on neat lavender oil. Cover with a soft, dry dressing.

CATARRH

ESSENTIAL OILS: Peppermint, tea tree, rosemary
TREATMENT: Inhalation using a blend of the oils. Chest and throat massage using a total of 6 drops of the above blended oils in 1 tablespoon vegetable oil.

CHILBLAINS

ESSENTIAL OILS: Lemon, lavender, rosemary
TREATMENT: Massage initially with neat lavender oil. Make a blend of 6 drops of the above oils with 1 tablespoon vegetable oil and massage daily.

COLD SORES

ESSENTIAL OILS: Geranium, tea tree or lavender
TREATMENT: Apply neat to the sore.

CONSTIPATION

ESSENTIAL OILS: Black pepper, palmarosa
TREATMENT: Make a massage oil containing 3 drops of each of the above oils in 1 tablespoon vegetable oil. Massage the abdomen daily in a clockwise direction.

COUGHS AND COLDS

ESSENTIAL OILS: Eucalyptus, thyme, lemon, rosemary
TREATMENT: Use the above oils in a bath, and for massage and inhalation.

CRAMPS, MUSCLES

ESSENTIAL OILS: Lavender, black pepper, rosemary
TREATMENT: Blend above oils with vegetable oil for massage. Use 3 drops of each essential oil in a bath.

CUTS

ESSENTIAL OILS: Lavender, tea tree
TREATMENT: Apply a compress using either of the above oils to stop bleeding and prevent infection. Leave open to the air unless severe. If needed, put 2 drops of either oil on a dressing to cover the cut.

CYSTITIS

ESSENTIAL OILS: Bergamot, benzoin, cedarwood
TREATMENT: 1 drop bergamot, 1 drop benzoin, 2 drops cedarwood in 2 teaspoons vegetable oil to massage over the bladder. 3 drops of each in a hot bath.

DERMATITIS

ESSENTIAL OILS: Chamomile, lavender, cedarwood
TREATMENT: 3 drops of each in a bath. 2 drops of each in 2 teaspoons vegetable oil as a topical application.

EARACHE

ESSENTIAL OILS: Tea tree, garlic
TREATMENT: 3 drops tea tree or garlic oil in 1 teaspoon olive oil warmed to lukewarm (no hotter). Drop a few drops into the ear. Plug the external opening of the ear with cotton wool.

ECZEMA

ESSENTIAL OILS: Bergamot, lavender, chamomile.
TREATMENT: See DERMATITIS

EXHAUSTION

Physical

ESSENTIAL OILS: Lavender, peppermint, geranium
TREATMENT: In a bath or use in a massage. Inhale the scent of the blended oils.

Nervous

ESSENTIAL OILS: Frankincense, peppermint, clary sage
TREATMENT: See PHYSICAL

Fainting

ESSENTIAL OILS: Marjoram or lavender
TREATMENT: Put a few drops of oil on a tissue and hold under the nose of the faint person or let the person sniff directly from the oil bottle.

FATIGUE

ESSENTIAL OILS: Lemon, clary sage, lavender.
TREATMENT: See EXHAUSTION

FEVER

ESSENTIAL OILS: Black pepper, lavender, peppermint
TREATMENT: Hot bath. Massage.

FIBROSITIS

ESSENTIAL OILS: Black pepper, peppermint, rosemary
TREATMENT: Massage.

FLU

ESSENTIAL OILS: Tea tree, peppermint, black pepper
TREATMENT: See FEVER

GLANDULAR FEVER

ESSENTIAL OILS: Cypress, tea tree, lemon
TREATMENT: Bath. Massage the chest and the glands in the neck using 2 drops of each oil in 2 teaspoons olive oil.

GOUT

ESSENTIAL OILS: Benzoin, juniper, rosemary
TREATMENT: Bath. Massage.

GUM INFECTIONS

ESSENTIAL OILS: Tea tree, myrrh
TREATMENT: Mouthwash using either or both oils.

HAEMORRHOIDS

ESSENTIAL OILS: Cypress, juniper, geranium
TREATMENT: Add 2 drops of each oil to half a bowlful (large enough to sit in) of warm water. Agitate the water to disperse the oils. Sit in the water for 10–15 minutes. Follow with 1 drop of each oil in 1 tablespoon olive oil, used to gently massage the haemorrhoids.

HAY FEVER

ESSENTIAL OILS: Lavender, lemon, geranium, hyssop
TREATMENT: Inhalation. Bath.

HEADACHE AND MIGRAINE

Nerves
ESSENTIAL OILS: Lavender, marjoram
TREATMENT: Bath. Inhalation. Neck and temple massage.

Gastric

ESSENTIAL OILS: Peppermint
TREATMENT: Massage over stomach and abdomen. Inhalation. Bath.

HEARTBURN

ESSENTIAL OILS: Peppermint
TREATMENT: Mix 1 drop of peppermint oil with 1 teaspoon honey in a cup. Fill the cup with warm water, mixing well. Sip the drink slowly.

HOARSENESS AND VOICE LOSS

ESSENTIAL OILS: Cypress, sandalwood, thyme
TREATMENT: Gargle, inhalation, throat massage.

IMMUNE SYSTEM BOOSTER

ESSENTIAL OILS: Tea tree, garlic, eucalyptus, thyme
TREATMENT: Bath, massage, inhalation.

INDIGESTION

ESSENTIAL OILS:
Peppermint, ginger
TREATMENT: Mix 1 drop of either oil with 1 teaspoon honey in a cup. Fill the cup with warm water, mixing well. Sip the drink slowly.

INFLAMMATION OF TISSUES

ESSENTIAL OILS: Chamomile, lavender, sandalwood
TREATMENT: Cold compress.

INSOMNIA

ESSENTIAL OILS: Lemon balm, chamomile, lavender, marjoram
TREATMENT: Bath. Massage. Air spray.

MENOPAUSE

Hot Flushes
ESSENTIAL OILS: clary sage, geranium, lime
TREATMENT: Bath. Massage. Air spray.

Depression
ESSENTIAL OILS: Ylang-ylang, clary sage, bergamot
TREATMENT: See HOT FLUSHES

MENSTRUAL

Cramps
ESSENTIAL OILS: Bergamot, clary sage, cypress
TREATMENT: See MENOPAUSE

Heavy Loss
ESSENTIAL OILS: Cypress, rose, chamomile
TREATMENT: See MENOPAUSE

Irregular
ESSENTIAL OILS: Clary sage, marjoram, chamomile
TREATMENT: See MENOPAUSE

Painful
ESSENTIAL OILS: Juniper, clary sage, marjoram
TREATMENT: See MENOPAUSE

Scanty
ESSENTIAL OILS: Myrrh, marjoram, clary sage
TREATMENT: See MENOPAUSE

MOUTH ULCERS

ESSENTIAL OILS: Myrrh, clary sage
TREATMENT: Mouthwash.

MUCUS

ESSENTIAL OILS: Benzoin, black pepper, tea tree
TREATMENT: Inhalation. Bath. Chest massage.

NAUSEA AND VOMITING

ESSENTIAL OILS: Peppermint, lavender
TREATMENT: See HEARTBURN

NERVOUS TENSION

ESSENTIAL OILS: Basil, marjoram, sandalwood
TREATMENT: Bath. Massage. Air spray.

PREMENSTRUAL SYNDROME (PMS)

Nerves and Mood Swings
ESSENTIAL OILS: Chamomile, geranium, marjoram, rose
TREATMENT: See NERVOUS TENSION

Water Retention
ESSENTIAL OILS: Fennel, juniper, rosemary
TREATMENT: Massage. Bath.

PSORIASIS

ESSENTIAL OILS: Bergamot, lavender
TREATMENT: Facial steam (if problem is on the face). Bath. Add 6 drops mixed oils in 1 tablespoon sweet almond oil. Use to massage on troubled areas.

RASHES

ESSENTIAL OILS: Chamomile, lavender, tea tree
TREATMENT: Ointment, baths, compresses. Massage, see PSORIASIS.

RHEUMATISM

ESSENTIAL OILS: Juniper, pine, rosemary
TREATMENT: Baths. Massage.

RINGWORM

ESSENTIAL OILS: Tea tree, myrrh, lavender
TREATMENT: Ointment containing some or all of the oils. Tea tree applied neat.

SCABIES

ESSENTIAL OILS: Lemon, peppermint, thyme
TREATMENT: See RINGWORM

SCAR TISSUE

ESSENTIAL OILS: Frankincense, lavender, sandalwood, myrrh
TREATMENT: 1 drop each essential oil in 2 teaspoons wheat germ oil, massage twice daily as long as needed.

SHOCK

ESSENTIAL OILS: Neroli, peppermint, mandarin, ylang-ylang
TREATMENT: Inhalation. Bath. Massage.

SPRAINS AND STRAINS

ESSENTIAL OILS: Chamomile, lavender, rosemary
TREATMENT: Cold compress.

STIFFNESS, MUSCLES AND JOINTS

ESSENTIAL OILS: Black pepper, lavender, rosemary
TREATMENT: Massage. Bath.

SUNBURN

ESSENTIAL OILS: Lavender
TREATMENT: Bath. Massage oil gently smoothed on burns.

THROAT, SORE

ESSENTIAL OILS: Clary sage, geranium, lavender
TREATMENT: Inhalation. Gargle.

TONSILLITIS

ESSENTIAL OILS: Bergamot, hyssop, thyme
TREATMENT: See THROAT, SORE

TRAVEL SICKNESS

See HEARTBURN
Drink half an hour before journey commences.

VARICOSE VEINS

ESSENTIAL OILS: Bergamot, cypress, lemon
TREATMENT: Cold compress using 6 drops mixed essential oils in 2 teaspoons witch hazel extract.

WARTS AND VERRUCAE

ESSENTIAL OILS: Tea tree
TREATMENT: Drip neat oil onto wart or verruca.

WOUNDS AND SORES

ESSENTIAL OILS: Chamomile, lavender, tea tree
TREATMENT: Wound wash. Dry dressing with a few drops neat lavender or tea tree oil dropped on a pad.

AROMATIC BATHS

There are many different types of baths in which we may use essential oils beneficially: foot bath, hand bath, sitz bath, half-full bath and a full bath.

The preparations below contain only essential oils. They can be mixed in larger quantities when you find your favourite; oil blends improve with age.

Don't be tempted to use more than 8–10 drops in a full bath, less in the other types.

To avoid floating 'hot spots' of unmixed oil, it's best to mix the oils with either one tablespoon full-cream milk or almond oil before adding to the bath.

BATHTIME BLENDS

Antibacterial
3 drops tea tree oil, 2 drops eucalyptus oil, 2 drops thyme oil, 1 drop lemon oil, 1 drop clove oil

Antiviral
3 drops tea tree oil, 3 drops eucalyptus oil, 3 drops lavender oil, 1 drop thyme oil

Deodorising
4 drops sage oil, 2 drops eucalyptus oil, 2 drops tea tree oil, 2 drops peppermint oil

Dry Skin
4 drops chamomile oil, 4 drops geranium oil, 2 drops patchouli oil

Greasy Skin
5 drops lemon oil, 3 drops ylang-ylang oil, 2 drops cypress oil

Spotty Skin
2 drops eucalyptus oil, 2 drops thyme oil, 4 drops lavender oil, 2 drops chamomile oil

Rejuvenating
4 drops lavender oil, 3 drops rosemary oil, 2 drops peppermint oil

Relaxing
4 drops chamomile oil, 3 drops lavender oil, 3 drops ylang-ylang oil

Rise and Shine
2 drops bergamot oil, 3 drops orange oil, 3 drops lemon oil, 1 drop peppermint oil, 1 drop cinnamon oil

Slimming
3 drops sage oil, 3 drops petitgrain oil, 2 drops grapefruit oil, 2 drops lavender oil

Sunburn
8–10 drops lavender oil

Sleep Well
4 drops chamomile oil, 2 drops lavender oil, 2 drops marjoram oil, 2 drops sandalwood oil

Just Ahhhh!
1 drop lavender oil, 2 drops grapefruit oil, 2 drops geranium oil, 2 drops ylang-ylang oil, 2 drops patchouli oil

MASSAGE AND ESSENTIAL OILS

Massage is probably the best known way of employing essential oils and certainly there are few more luxurious and relaxing ways to experience the perfume and healing properties of the oils. Massage is a very special experience: it can be healing; strengthening; relaxing; sensual or energising; and should always be a loving, sharing, trusting time. You don't have to wait for someone else to give you a massage – these oils can be used as an after-bath or shower oil, massaged well into the skin of the whole body, or a few drops can be added to a bath as a bath oil.

Massage oil should be fairly light so that the skin isn't left feeling greasy, but vitamin and mineral rich oils may be added in small quantities. I like to add a little (about 1cm/^{1}/$_2$in) of alcohol after bottling the finished oil – it floats on top of the oil helping to preserve it. The alcohol also assists with the penetration of the oil into the skin.

The recipe which follows is for 100ml (3^1/$_3$fl oz) of massage oil. Choose the essential oils from the recipes which follow or make up your own blend.

Basic Massage Oil

50ml (1^2/$_3$fl oz) grape seed oil or Basic Herb Oil
1 tablespoon olive oil
2 teaspoons almond oil
2 teaspoons avocado oil
1 teaspoon wheat germ oil
40 drops essential oil chosen from the following recipes

Mix all the oils in a 100ml (3^1/$_3$fl oz) bottle. Shake well to mix. Add about 1cm (^{1}/$_2$in) alcohol (vodka is suitable).

After-sport Rub

This oil will help to ease the pain of sore muscles after strenuous sport.

1 teaspoon clove oil
1 teaspoon eucalyptus oil
1 teaspoon thyme oil
1 teaspoon black pepper oil
1 teaspoon lavender oil

Mix all the oils in a 25ml (about 1fl oz) bottle. Shake well. Add 40 drops to 100ml (3^1/$_3$fl oz) of Basic Massage Oil.

Relaxation and Depression Lifter

This oil will help to lift and calm the spirits. This blend can be used in a warm bath (10 drops), and then followed by a soothing massage.

^{1}/$_2$ teaspoon sandalwood oil
^{1}/$_2$ teaspoon chamomile oil
2 teaspoons ylang-ylang oil
1 teaspoon lavender oil
1 teaspoon orange oil

Mix all the oils in a 25ml (about 1fl oz) bottle. Shake well. Add 40 drops to 100ml (3^1/$_3$fl oz) of Basic Massage Oil.

Post-viral Syndrome Chaser

(Myalgic Encephalomyelitis)

This distressing complaint can cause aching muscles, headaches, extreme exhaustion, mental confusion, loss of memory and many more symptoms. Ease the misery by using this blend daily as an after-shower or bath massage oil and by being given a massage as often as possible.

1 teaspoon grapefruit oil
1 teaspoon black pepper oil
1 teaspoon thyme oil
1 teaspoon cypress oil
1 teaspoon rosemary oil

Mix all the oils in a 25ml (about 1fl oz) bottle. Shake well. Add 40 drops to 100ml ($3^1/_3$fl oz) of Basic Massage Oil.

Work-related Stress

This blend is for those of you who spend a large part of your lives with workmates, computers, telephones, traffic and stressful environments. It's hard to relax at the end of the day when we should be having some peaceful time with our families. Use this blend to help with the 'unwinding' process.

2 teaspoons melissa (lemon balm) oil
$^1/_2$ teaspoon benzoin oil
1 teaspoon bergamot oil
1 teaspoon lavender oil
$^1/_2$ teaspoon geranium oil
1 teaspoon ylang-ylang oil

Mix all the oils in a 25ml (about 1fl oz) bottle. Shake well. Add 40 drops to 100ml ($3^1/_3$fl oz) of Basic Massage Oil.

Family Oil

This blend is suitable for the whole family — after all, the adults aren't the only ones who suffer from stress or who enjoy a massage. The oils will de-stress, calm and uplift.

1 teaspoon lavender oil
1 teaspoon lemon oil
1 teaspoon geranium oil
1 teaspoon bergamot oil
$^1/_2$ teaspoon mandarin oil
$^1/_2$ teaspoon sandalwood oil

Mix all the oils in a 25ml (about 1fl oz) bottle. Shake well. Add 40 drops to 100ml ($3^1/_3$fl oz) of Basic Massage Oil.

OTHER USES

Anti-mosquito Blend

Another use for essential oils. This blend may be used both on the body and in the air to keep mosquitoes at bay. See also Blending Guide at the beginning of this chapter.

> 1 teaspoon citronella oil
> 1 teaspoon lemon grass oil
> 2 teaspoons lavender oil
> ½ teaspoon peppermint oil
> ½ teaspoon thyme oil

Mix all the oils in a 25ml (about 1fl oz) bottle. Store in a cool dark place.

To Use as a Room Spray: Follow the directions in the Blending Guide – at the beginning of this chapter.

To Use on the Body: Put 25 drops in a 50ml ($1^2/3$fl oz) bottle, add 2 teaspoons vodka or witch hazel extract, and fill with grape seed or almond oil. Shake well before rubbing onto exposed parts of the body.

COLOGNES USING ESSENTIAL OILS

These colognes are fun to make and I hope these recipes will inspire you to make your own personalised perfume. Colognes can be used as perfume, after-bath or shower splashes, an aftershave for men or as a light deodorant. They need to mature in a dark place for 2–3 months. Shake them often and keep trying a little on the inside of your wrist. You will be astonished how the perfumes change as they mature.

Combine the oils and vodka in the following blends in a 100ml ($3^1/3$fl oz) bottle.

COLOGNE BLENDS

Sensual
4 drops patchouli oil
5 drops ylang-ylang oil
1 drop clove oil
100ml ($3^1/3$fl oz) vodka

Moonlight
5 drops ylang-ylang oil
3 drops rose geranium oil
3 drops patchouli oil
100ml ($3^1/3$fl oz) vodka

Silk Lady
6 drops lavender oil
3 drops rose geranium oil
1 drop clove oil
100ml ($3^1/3$fl oz) vodka

Fresh and Lemony
2 drops petitgrain oil
2 drops lime oil
2 drops lemon grass oil
2 drops lemon oil
1 drop clove oil
100ml ($3^1/3$fl oz) vodka

Girl Next Door
3 drops lavender oil
1 drop cinnamon oil
1 drop patchouli oil
2 drops geranium oil
1 drop clove oil
2 drops bergamot oil
100ml ($3^1/3$fl oz) vodka

AROMATHERAPY MAGIC

Some people believe particular oil blends have magical properties, and some use the blends to facilitate 'visualisation' (i.e. the calling up of mental images).

Oil blends may be used in diffusers, incense and sprays, or for sniffing (use a few drops on cotton wool) – they are not for drinking. Oils diffuse nicely into the air if a few drops are placed on light globes, warm radiators, wood in open fires and anywhere that there is heat.

Don't worry if you don't have all the oils in a recipe. It's perfectly all right to increase the amounts of the other oils or to look at ABC of Essential Oils earlier in this chapter and choose oils with similar qualities.

MAGICAL BLENDS

The following blends should be mixed in a 25ml (about 1fl oz) bottle, and stored in a cool dark place.

To Raise Magical Powers
1 teaspoon nutmeg oil, 1 teaspoon bay oil, 1 teaspoon orange oil, 1 teaspoon sage oil

To Lift Depression
1 teaspoon basil oil, 1 teaspoon clary sage oil, 1 teaspoon melissa oil, 2 teaspoons ylang-ylang oil

To Heal
1 teaspoon eucalyptus oil, 1 teaspoon tea tree oil, 1 teaspoon cypress oil, 1 teaspoon pine oil, 1 teaspoon sandalwood oil

To Bring Love
1 teaspoon rosemary oil, 1 teaspoon lavender oil, 40 drops coriander oil, 40 drops lemon verbena oil, 2 teaspoons ylang-ylang oil

For the Brain and Memory
2 teaspoons rosemary oil, 2 teaspoons sage oil, 1 teaspoon clove oil

CHAPTER SIX
HERBS IN THE KITCHEN

Outside the courtyard, near the entrance gates, is a great garden of four acres with a fence running round on either side. Here grow tall flourishing fruit trees: pears, pomegranates and shining apples, sweet figs and luxuriant olives. The fruit of these trees never falls off or fails, but is there winter and summer, all the year round; for the west wind, always blowing, forms new fruit while it ripens others. Pear after pear comes to maturity and apple after apple, one bunch of grapes after another and fig after fig. There, too, a fruitful vineyard has been planted, of which one part, in a warm level spot exposed to the sun, is a drying ground, and elsewhere some grapes are being gathered and others trodden. In front there are unripe grapes only now shedding their blossom, while others are already turning colour. There too, beyond the furthest row of vines are well kept beds of herbs which are fresh all the year round, and there are two springs, one of which sprinkles the whole garden, while the other is channelled under the entrance of the courtyard to issue by the lofty palace and here the townsfolk draw their water. These were the splendid gifts of the gods in the house of Alcinous.

HOMER, *THE ODYSSEY*, BOOK VII

M ake your food a herbal event – it doesn't take any more preparation time and will change 'dull' to 'delicious'. Herbs can be used in flower and green salads, teas, seasonings, cakes, desserts and main meals and by adding herbs to these foods we can help to ensure that our meals are attractive, tasty and digestible. Herbs add distinction and more; oregano and thyme are also digestives, peppermint and spearmint help to dispel wind, the seeds and feathery fronds of fennel help to digest fat.

When we sold the 'Rivendell Skincare' business I was left with time on my hands. I cast around for something to do and an old ambition of mine surfaced – to run a restaurant. This seemed an unrealistic thing to do as we were 30 kilometres from the nearest town but, as ever, the prospect of a challenge was exciting. We rebuilt the kitchen, enlarged a room overlooking the valley, bought quantities of crockery and cutlery and indulged in moments of blind panic. In a few weeks 'The Prancing Pony' restaurant was open. We learnt a whole new way of using herbs. The emphasis in the past had been on their medicinal and skin care properties, and the cooking aspect, while acknowledged, had never been really explored.

To many people the word 'herb' means a sprig of parsley decorating a plate of food, sage used in poultry stuffing or a pinch of mixed dried herbs in a stew. We found excitement in discovering innovative ways of using herbs, and our restaurant was often something of a food revelation to visitors. Even the 'after-dinner mints' were peppermint leaves dipped in chocolate!

We provided each table with a small dish of fennel seeds for guests to nibble after their meal and the floral decorations on the tables were small delicate bunches of herbs. The view from the windows was always changing: placid black cows in the valley, heads down in the rain, grazing before darkness fell; a crescent moon rising above the gum trees and kangaroos venturing out on the hills to feed in the safety of the coming night. Sometimes there was mist in the valley and the farmhouse would seem to float on an island

TOP: Chopping fresh herbs
MIDDLE: Clockwise from bottom left: Summer Quencher, Sleepy Time, Comforter, Pregnancy, Elder Tisane
BOTTOM: Angelic Pie

surrounded by grey swirling sea. It was always different, always lovely.

The old saying 'You are what you eat' is only partly true. It needs a great deal more than just food to create a holistically healthy person, but food does form a good foundation on which to build. Herbs used in cooking and in drinks can have many benefits.

◆ They can add vitamins and minerals to the diet. Unless you grow your own unsprayed vegetables or buy them direct from an organic grower you are likely to be getting a good dose of chemicals and not many of the vitamins. By the time the vegetables have been through the hands of the grower, the retailer, the wholesaler and finally yours, enough time has elapsed for them to be little more than a good source of fibre. Vitamins and minerals are not the only active substances to be found in herbs. Other constituents work on the body in a very subtle way, improving and strengthening every function.

◆ Herbs can be used to replace salt as a flavouring agent. This is good for everyone but particularly those on salt-restricted diets. We have included a basic recipe for a Herb Salt which you can adapt to suit your family. This is healthier than commercial 'herb salts' on the market, which tend to consist of salt with a few ground herbs added. Other herbs, such as angelica can help to sweeten food, making it easier to reduce our intake of sugar. Or they can be used as a sugar substitute for those on a sugar-free diet.

◆ By adding herbs to your cooking you are using them in a preventive way. For instance, caraway added to cabbage, or coriander to beans during cooking helps to prevent flatulence as well as giving the dish a delicious flavour. This seems to make more sense than drinking a cup of caraway tea after the meal to cure the discomfort.

◆ The use of herbs can transform a 'good plain meal' into a gastronomic delight. Many people enjoy roast potatoes but take them for granted. Sprinkle them with chopped rosemary before roasting, then sit back and wait for the compliments. Such simple things can transform you from an 'average' cook into an excellent and innovative one.

TOP: From top: Nasturtium Kebabs, Herbed Eggplant
MIDDLE: The Very Best Tomato Ketchup
BOTTOM: Lemon Balm and Mint Fruit Salad

EATING YOUR WAY TO HEALTH

Vitamins are organic substances present in minute amounts in foods. They are essential for health, and are also responsible for the assimilation of some minerals. Minerals, in their turn, help in the assimilation and functioning of vitamins as well as providing the body with necessary elements. The way in which vitamins and minerals function is extremely complex. For instance, iron is assimilated more easily from meat, but a high-protein diet (such as one including a lot of meat) would increase the need for this mineral. Vitamin C increases the assimilation of iron from vegetables but decreases its availability in meat and also decreases the assimilation of copper.

Some people take vitamin and mineral supplements in the mistaken idea that this enables them to eat any amount of rubbish, because the pills will take care of them, but vitamins and minerals are not substitutes for proteins, carbohydrates and fats. In fact, they need these nutrients in order to be assimilated into the body. Without a balanced diet, the most assiduous taking of supplements will not give you good health. A balanced, wholesome diet, however, is becoming more difficult to achieve in these days of fast foods, preserved meats, pre-packaged foods, sprayed and stale vegetables and, often, terrible water.

Thankfully, there is a growing awareness of these problems and we are now able to find (sometimes after a long search) free-range eggs, 'organically' grown vegetables and grains, and other foods which we can trust.

Food should be fun to cook and delicious for the whole family. If you are eating brown rice and vegetables every day of the week, your chances of keeping well (and sane) may not be as good as they should be. You would soon drive your family from the dining table to the nearest pizza parlour. The best nutrition comes from eating a wide variety of foods. This has the additional benefit of preventing the build-up of some allergies.

VITAMIN AND MINERALS IN HERBS

All herbs contain some vitamins and minerals in varying amounts.
The following list is of those herbs which are the best source.

VITAMINS

A	Alfalfa, dandelion greens, nettle, watercress
B1 (THIAMINE)	Dandelion greens, sunflower seeds, thyme
B2 (RIBOFLAVIN)	Dandelion greens, thyme, watercress
B3 (NIACIN)	Anise, dandelion greens, landcress
B5 (PANTOTHENIC ACID)	Catnep, dandelion greens, nettle
B6 (PYRIDOXINE)	Anise, dandelion greens
B12 (COBALAMIN)	Alfalfa
BIOTIN	Alfalfa, dandelion greens, thyme, watercress
CHOLINE	Alfalfa, dandelion greens, nettle, parsley, watercress
FOLIC ACID	Red raspberry
C	Most herbs but particularly dandelion greens, parsley and watercress
D (ERGOCALCIFEROL)	Alfalfa, landcress and watercress, nettle, red raspberry
E (TOCOPHEROL)	Alfalfa, dandelion greens, landcress and watercress, red raspberry
K (QUINONES)	Alfalfa, yarrow
P (RUTIN)	Lemon peel, nettle, red raspberry, rue

MINERALS

CALCIUM	Alfalfa, anise, dandelion greens, nettle, watercress
CHLORINE	Most herbs
FLUORINE	Garlic, landcress and watercress, sage
IODINE	Cayenne, peppermint
IRON	Dandelion greens, garlic, landcress and watercress, nettle, parsley
MAGNESIUM	Cayenne, dandelion greens, parsley, red clover, watercress
MANGANESE	Land and watercress, nettle, red clover
PHOSPHORUS	Alfalfa, cayenne, dandelion greens, garlic, sage, watercress
POTASSIUM	Dandelion greens, parsley, watercress
SILICON	Dandelion greens, parsley, watercress
SULPHUR	Cayenne, garlic, landcress and watercress, nettle, parsley
ZINC	Dandelion greens, garlic, nettle, rosemary

HERB TEAS

We drink for many reasons: to quench thirst, to warm or cool ourselves, to share companionship with friends and to comfort ourselves. In the case of herb teas, there is the additional benefit of the therapeutic properties to be gained. Tea and coffee have a valuable role as stimulants but, unfortunately, we often drink them to excess and the stimulating properties can become destructive to the nerves and body, leaving us feeling 'jumpy' and with an 'acid' stomach. If we try to limit the intake of tea and coffee to about three cups a day, drinking herbal infusions or decoctions the rest of the time, we are getting the best from both types of drinks.

GETTING TO KNOW THE HERB TEAS

It can be unwise to stick to one single herb or blend of herbs until you are absolutely sure of what you are doing. Continual use of any particular herb may aggravate the very symptoms which you are trying to alleviate. For instance, a young woman came to see me complaining of headaches. During our conversation she said, 'I've been drinking eight to ten cups of peppermint tea each day for weeks, but my headaches seem to get worse, not better.' Of course the condition would worsen, as peppermint contains powerful constituents and her body was reacting to an overdose of these properties. If you don't thoroughly understand the properties of the herbs you are using, you may unwittingly overstimulate certain organs or functions of the body, so try to vary the types of drinks, especially at first. Making mixtures of the herbs helps overcome the problem and creates the excitement of discovery as you make and taste a new and unique blend.

You can use honey to sweeten the teas if you like. Honey rots teeth in the same way as sugar but it contains many valuable minerals, enzymes, and organic acids. It also acts as a disinfectant, protecting against bacterial and fungal infections.

With such valuable attributes, cleaning your teeth after eating or drinking is a small price to pay. Try to buy honey direct from an apiarist or, failing this, ask your health food store where the honey comes from and whether or not it has been heated or treated in any way. It is best to get the 'least-messed-about-with' honey.

MAKING HERB TEAS

Herbs for tea-making should be chopped or crushed until the pieces resemble Indian tea in size. Store the mixtures in glass jars away from the light, keeping out only enough for immediate use. In this way you will preserve the flavour, colour and goodness for as long as a year. Keep a separate teapot or infuser for herbal drinks, as tannin residue from other teas can alter the delicate flavour of the herbs. Lemon rind and juice and orange peel can be added to any teas to improve flavour and increase vitamin and mineral content.

Some teas can be made as an infusion, like conventional tea, just by pouring boiling water over the flowers, leaves, seeds or root and leaving it to stand for a few minutes. Some need to be simmered, as a decoction, to draw out enough flavour and goodness from the herb. Either way, much of the therapeutic value of herb teas is in the essential oils which will evaporate off in steam. It's important to cover the mug or pot to prevent loss of these oils.

The Herb Teas Chart will help you to make blends of tea to suit your own palate and needs. Try small amounts at first. When you find a mix you like, you can make it in bulk. Make these drinks using fresh or dried herbs but remember, if you want a specific mix, dried herbs will ensure that you have the same blend throughout the year.

RIGHT: Herb teas

HERB TEAS CHART

ACTION HERBS TO USE

ANTACID

Alfalfa sprouts, lemon juice, nettle leaves, red clover sprouts

APPETITE DEPRESSANT

Anise or fennel seeds, crushed, or parsley leaves

APPETITE STIMULANT

Alfalfa or red clover sprouts, calendula flowers, ginger root, lemon rind or juice, nettle, tarragon or thyme leaves

ANTI-DEPRESSANT

Chamomile flowers, sage leaves

BREATH FRESHENER

Anise, coriander, dill or fennel seeds, lemon rind or juice, orange peel, peppermint, rosemary, sage or thyme leaves.

BLOOD CLEANSER

Alfalfa or red clover sprouts, bergamot, elder, peppermint, nettle or yarrow leaves, lemon juice or rind

BOWEL

Calendula flowers, dill or fennel seeds, ginger root, lemon rind or juice, raspberry leaves or red clover sprouts.

BODY WARMING

Anise seeds, bergamot, lemon balm, peppermint or sage leaves, calendula or elderflower, ginger root, lemon rind or juice, yarrow leaves or flowers

COUGHS

Lemon rind or juice, mullein, raspberry or sage leaves, red clover sprouts

DIGESTION AID

Angelica leaves or root, anise or caraway seeds, lemon juice, mallow root, marjoram or savory leaves

FLATULENCE

Anise, caraway, coriander or dill seeds, chamomile flowers, ginger or mallow root, peppermint or thyme leaves, orange peel

HANGOVER

Chamomile flowers or thyme leaves

HEADACHES

Ginger root or lemon balm, marjoram, peppermint, parsley, rosemary or sage leaves

HYSTERICS

Chamomile flowers, lemon balm leaves or valerian root

INSOMNIA

Chamomile flowers, catnep, sage or tarragon leaves

IRRITABILITY

Anise or caraway seeds, borage leaves or flowers, calendula or chamomile flowers, lemon balm leaves, lemon juice, orange peel, valerian root

LOW ENERGY

Borage leaves or flowers, rosemary leaves

MENSTRUAL PAIN

Anise or caraway seeds, chamomile flowers, ginger root, catnep, lemon balm, marjoram, peppermint, nettle, raspberry or thyme leaves

MORNING SICKNESS

Anise or caraway seeds, chamomile flowers, ginger root, basil, bergamot, lemon balm, marjoram, peppermint or raspberry leaves

MOUTH SORES

Mallow root, raspberry, sage or thyme leaves

NAUSEA

Alfalfa sprouts, basil, peppermint or raspberry leaves, ginger root

NERVE TONIC

Chamomile or elderflower, lemon balm, peppermint, rosemary or thyme leaves, valerian root

NIGHTMARES

Chamomile flowers, marjoram leaves, oregano leaves or flowers

REFRESHMENT

Bergamot, lemon balm or lemon grass leaves, borage leaves or flowers, lemon rind or juice or orange peel

RELAXATION

Chamomile or elderflower, lemon balm, marjoram, oregano, sage or tarragon leaves

STOMACH UPSETS

Alfalfa sprouts, angelica leaves or root, caraway seeds, mallow root, orange peel, savory or thyme leaves

THIRST-QUENCHING

Basil or borage leaves or root, lemon grass leaves, lemon rind or juice

Cautions:

Borage/mullein

The hairs on the leaves of these plants can cause contact dermatitis and also stomach problems. Use gloves to pick the leaves if you are sensitive. Strain the tea through a coffee filter to avoid ingesting hairs.

Nettle

Old plants need to be well cooked as they contain a principle which could cause kidney damage if eaten raw.

Parsley

Avoid using as a tea if pregnant or if the kidneys are inflamed. The small amount normally used in cooking and salads is safe.

Rosemary/sage/thyme

Not to be used in large quantities or for an extended period of time.

Yarrow

Extended use may make the skin light-sensitive resulting in pigmentation.

Valerian

Extended use may have a depressant effect. Take no more than twice a day for 6 days. Repeat for three weeks only.

TONIC

Alfalfa or red clover sprouts, angelica leaves or root, anise seeds, mallow root, orange peel, basil, bergamot, peppermint, nettle, parsley, raspberry, rosemary, sage, savory leaves

TOXICITY

Alfalfa sprouts, caraway or fennel seeds, basil or nettle leaves, ginger root

VITAMIN AND MINERAL SUPPLEMENT

Alfalfa or red clover sprouts, anise seeds, catnep, lemon grass, nettle, parsley, raspberry, sage, tarragon, thyme, yarrow leaves, lemon rind or juice, orange peel, mallow root

MAKING YOUR OWN HERB TEAS

To create herbal mixtures you will need to know the individual taste of each herb. As with any experiments you make, you will need to keep records if you are to be able to repeat your successes. In your record book, you might list down the side of a page the herbs which you have available and put headings across the top, such as bland, lemony, bitter, sweet and full-bodied. Leave the last column for comments. Fill in the columns using a pencil so that you can rub out easily and note successes and disasters, to guide your future efforts.

First, try making a tea using one herb (noting the name and amount in your book) with maybe a bland or a lemony flavour. If this is not very exciting, try adding another herb, perhaps a full-bodied or bitter one. You will quickly get the 'feel' of blending after making a few mixes.

I work in a fairly haphazard way, using a quarter of a cup of boiling water and adding pinches of herbs until the taste is to my liking. You can be more scientific if you like. The important thing is the end result, but don't forget to note down what you used, whichever way you do it! Some of these recipes are teas for particular conditions, others for pleasure. You may like to try each tea and then add or substitute your own flavours. If you have a source of unsprayed oranges and lemons, you can grate and dry the rind (zest) for use in drinks, cakes and desserts. All these teas are made using the infusion method, see Infusion or Tea.

HERB TEA BLENDS

Pregnancy

1 part ginger root
1 part liquorice
2 parts nettle
1 part mallow, root or leaf
1 part yellow dock
4 parts raspberry

Sleepy Time

2 parts chamomile
2 parts lemon balm
2 parts nettle
2 parts liquorice
1 part catnep
1 part elderflower

Comforter

2 parts peppermint
1 part lemon balm
2 parts chamomile

Summer Quencher

For a delicious chilled drink, strain after 10 minutes, chill and add lemon juice and ice cubes.

3 parts lemon grass
2 parts lemon balm
2 parts borage leaf
2 parts lemon peel
1 part dill seed

Post-natal

4 parts raspberry
2 parts fennel
1 part borage
1/2 part dandelion root or leaf
1 part nettle
1 part dill
1/2 part mallow, root or leaf

Elder Tisane

6 parts elderflower
1 part caraway
2 parts red clover
1 part dried orange peel
1 part lemon balm

RIGHT: Clockwise from bottom left: Summer Quencher, Sleepy Time, Comforter, Pregnancy, Elder Tisane

THE GOURMET HERBALIST

I like to use fresh herbs whenever I can but this isn't always possible. Some herbs, such as tarragon, are winter dormant and others have specific times when they are at their best. If you have been very careful about the gathering, drying and storing, the dried herbs will be a good second best. A general rule is to use two or three times more fresh herb than dried.

Try using herbs in your favourite recipes. For instance, if you are making cheese scones, add a teaspoon of a finely chopped herb that complements the cheese. Note what you have done and the result. In this way you don't need to use new recipes but can improve those which your family already enjoys. It's easy to go overboard in the beginning, mixing too many herbs into too many dishes, leaving your taste buds totally confused. 'Easy does it' until you are familiar with the herbs and the way their flavours change or deepen when they are cooked. A young friend, new to cooking, decided once to make a very unusual soup for our lunch, so she added two tablespoons of liquorice powder as flavouring to the pot! We ended up eating herb omelettes and salad for lunch.

Many herbs need to be added towards the end of cooking as they can become bitter or lose vitamin and mineral content if cooked for too long. Using Herbs in the Kitchen will guide you until you are more at home with the herbs. A safe way to learn the amounts which suit your family is to add a little, taste, add more if you like and so on. After the recipes, you will find suggestions for mixtures of herbs (see Flavouring with Herbs). These are useful when you are in a hurry or when it's not convenient to use fresh.

USING HERBS IN THE KITCHEN

Not all herbs suggested should be used in each dish. I suggest a maximum of three or less.

Alfalfa and red clover sprouts are delicious and wholesome when included in dishes such as scrambled eggs, cheese on toast, omelettes, rice, soups, stews and casseroles. It's not necessary to cook them, toss a handful in before serving.

Those of you who wish to add less salt to their food may use a dried, powdered mixture of some or all of the following herbs. This adds natural sodium and flavour to the dishes. Add towards the end of cooking or as a sprinkle at the table: Angelica stem, borage, cayenne, chives, coriander seed, garlic, nettle, oregano, parsley, savories (both), thyme (common and lemon), watercress.

When cooking rice, use calendula petals instead of saffron to give a golden colour and subtle flavour.

USING HERBAL HONEYS

I like to use honey in herbal drinks and as often as possible in cooking. Flavoured honeys are delicious and healthy and they also make attractive gifts. To make them, heat the honey gently until it's runny, add 2 teaspoons of chopped herbs to each cup of honey and leave for a couple of weeks. Reheat, strain and pour into a jar. These honeys need refrigerating as the heating seems to destroy some of the natural keeping properties.

Ginger Honey

This ginger honey is good for cooking or for a hot herb and lemon drink (when you are cold and shivery or are coming down with a cold). This honey is wonderful for desserts, marinades and many other dishes.

Peel and chop 1 cup ginger root, put in a small pan and cover with honey. Bring to the boil and just simmer for about 1 hour. Strain and pour into a clean jar

USING HERBS IN COOKING

HOT DISHES

BEAN DISHES

Cayenne, coriander seed, garlic, oregano, parsley, sage, savories (both), thyme

BEEF

Bay, garlic, horseradish, hyssop, oregano, parsley, thyme

CABBAGE FAMILY

Aniseed, caraway seed, cayenne, dill seed, fennel seed, savories (both)

CARROTS

Aniseed, caraway seed, ginger, mints, parsley, thyme

CAULIFLOWER

Dill leaf, fennel leaf, parsley

CELERY

parsley

CHEESE DISHES

Basil, cayenne, chives, coriander leaf, nasturtium, parsley, savories (both), tarragon, thyme

CHICKEN

Bay, fennel leaf, garlic, ginger, lemon balm, lemon grass, oregano, parsley, rosemary, tarragon, lemon thyme

CURRIES

Basil, cayenne, coriander seed, garlic, ginger, lemon grass

EGGPLANT DISHES

Basil, cayenne, garlic, oregano, parsley, thyme

EGG DISHES

Basil, cayenne, horseradish, nasturtium, parsley, savories (both), tarragon, thyme (common and lemon)

FISH

Basil, bay, cayenne, coriander leaf, dill leaf, fennel leaf, garlic, hyssop, lemon balm, mints, oregano, parsley, savories (both), tarragon, thyme (common and lemon)

LAMB

Bay, cayenne, dill leaf, fennel leaf, garlic, hyssop, lemon balm, mints, oregano, parsley, rosemary, thyme (common and lemon)

MARROW, SQUASH, AND ZUCCHINI

Basil, cayenne, marjoram, parsley, thyme (common and lemon)

MUSHROOMS

Lemon balm, marjoram, parsley, sage, tarragon

OMELETTES

Cayenne, chives, dill and fennel leaves, oregano, parsley, rosemary

PEAS

Basil, dill leaf, mints, oregano, parsley, sage, savories (both)

POTATOES

Chives, dill leaf, mints, oregano, parsley, rosemary

RICE

Calendula petals, cayenne, coriander leaf, garlic, parsley, rosemary

SHELLFISH

Bay, chives, coriander leaf, garlic, marjoram, parsley, tarragon, thyme (common and lemon)

STEWED FRUIT

Angelica stem, aniseed, bergamot, borage (flowers as garnish), caraway seed, ginger, lemon balm, mints, nasturtium flowers (garnish)

STEWS

Basil, bay, cayenne, chives, garlic, horseradish, hyssop, marjoram, nettle (young heads), oregano, parsley, sage, savories (both), tarragon, common thyme

TOMATO DISHES

Basil, bay, fennel leaf, oregano, parsley, sage, common thyme

VEGETABLE HOTPOTS

See STEWS

VEGETABLE SOUPS

See STEWS

COLD DISHES

APPLES

Aniseed, basil, bergamot, lemon balm

AVOCADO

Basil, cayenne, garlic, horseradish, parsley, tarragon

BAKED CUSTARD

Ginger, lemon balm

BEAN SALAD

Garlic, parsley, summer savory, common thyme

BISCUITS

Aniseed, caraway seed, ginger, rosemary

CAKES

Caraway, ginger, peppermint, southernwood

CHICKEN

Parsley, rosemary, summer savory, tarragon

COTTAGE CHEESE

Basil, calendula petals, caraway seed, cayenne, chives, dill leaf, horseradish, nasturtium leaf, parsley, sage, summer savory, tarragon, common thyme

DRINKS, COLD

Angelica leaf, borage flowers, ginger, lemon balm, mints

EGGS, STUFFED

Cayenne, chives, horseradish, nasturtium leaves, parsley, summer savory

FLOWER SALADS

Bergamot petals, borage flowers, calendula petals, dandelion petals, nasturtium flowers, lemon thyme flowers

FRENCH DRESSING

Basil, chives, parsley, summer savory

FRUIT JUICES

Angelica stalk, borage flowers, lemon balm leaf, mints

GARNISHES

See FLOWER SALADS

GERMAN POTATO SALAD

Chives, dill leaf, parsley

HERB BUTTER

Chives, garlic, parsley, rosemary, summer savory, tarragon, thyme (common and lemon)

MAYONNAISE

Basil, cayenne, chives, garlic, horseradish, oregano, tarragon, lemon thyme

MUSHROOM SALAD

Basil, cayenne, chives, parsley, sage

POTATO SALAD

Basil, caraway seed, cayenne, chives, fennel leaf, oregano, tarragon

PUNCH

Angelica stem, borage flowers, lemon balm, mints, rosemary

RICE SALAD

Calendula petals, cayenne, chives, dill leaves, garlic, parsley, rosemary, tarragon

SALADS

Basil, bergamot leaf and flower, borage flowers, calendula petals, chives, cress (land and water), mints, nasturtium leaf and flower, parsley, thyme (common and lemon)

SANDWICHES

Basil, calendula petals, chives, cress (land and water), horseradish, nasturtium

TOMATO JUICE

Basil, cayenne, chives, fennel leaf, oregano, parsley, rosemary, tarragon

TOMATO SALAD

See TOMATO JUICE

TUNA

Cayenne, chives, dill leaf, fennel seed, horseradish, parsley

VEGETABLE JUICE

Basil, cayenne, fennel leaf, horseradish, oregano, parsley, rosemary, tarragon

VINEGARS

Basil, cayenne, chives, dill, garlic, ginger, horseradish, mint, rosemary, tarragon, thyme (common and lemon)

STORING HERBS

Herbs in jars on your kitchen shelf may look very attractive but too much light shortens their life so it's better to have small jars near the stove. These can be 'topped up' from the main store, which should be kept in a dark cupboard or in the freezer. Dried herbs are at their most effective for 12 months after drying. It's then time to empty your jars onto the garden or compost heap and begin storing the new season's crop.

STORING HERBS IN VINEGAR

When the annual or winter-dormant herbs (such as summer savory, basil and tarragon) are at their best, I store large quantities in vinegar to last through the winter. Make the vinegar like a tincture (see TINCTURES), using cider vinegar instead of water, and dilute it with fresh cider vinegar to taste.

Chopped fresh ginger and horseradish root store really well in vinegar or sherry and the resulting liquid is delicious to use in cooking.

STORING HERBS IN OIL

Drizzle some best quality olive oil in the bottom of a wide-mouthed crock or jar. Put in a layer of fresh, dry herb leaves. Drizzle more oil. Carry on in this way until all your leaves are stored. The last layer should be oil. The herbs will keep through winter and the oil may be used in cooking. The best herbs to treat in this way are basil and tarragon.

STORING HERBS IN SALT

Most herbs store well in salt, but use this method for herbs which don't dry or freeze well. Basil is an excellent herb to 'salt'. You will need a bag of cooking salt (with no additives) and a very wide-mouthed jar or crock. Put a layer of salt about 2.5cm (1in) deep in the bottom of the crock,

then 1cm (^{1}/$_2$in) herb leaves and 1cm (^{1}/$_2$in) salt. Continue until you have run out of herbs. Finish with 2.5cm (1in) salt. You can continue to add herbs to the pot as they become available.

When you need to use the herbs, simply lift out a few leaves, shake or rinse them and they are ready for use. A bonus of this method is the deliciously flavoured salt which you can use (in very small amounts) in your cooking.

FREEZING HERBS

Some herbs are best frozen, retaining flavour and colour which is almost as good as fresh. The best herbs to freeze are those which don't dry well, namely basil, coriander, chives, tarragon, lemon balm, parsley and mints. Try to avoid washing herbs which you are going to freeze. You can either strip the leaves off the stems or freeze whole sprigs. Put the herbs in a freezer bag, press down flat to expel the air, seal and freeze flat. It is very easy to break off the amount you need. Herbs are very limp after freezing so are suitable only for cooking. Chop the herbs easily while still frozen by crushing the leaves in your hands. It's very much harder to do once they have defrosted.

For attractive ice cubes which add delicate flavour to drinks, put borage flowers or mint leaves in ice cube trays, fill with water and freeze.

GARLIC PUREE

This will keep in the refrigerator for several weeks. The flavour is 'nutty' and not as overpowering as fresh garlic.

Place unpeeled cloves of garlic on an oiled baking tray and paint all over with oil. Bake at 180°C (350°F) until soft (10–15 minutes). Cool.

Squeeze the pulp into a small jar. Cover with olive oil.

DIPS AND CRACKERS

Cheese Ball

This decorative cheese ball can be served with Lebanese Crackers and makes a lovely table centre for a buffet meal. Use the same herbs plus either paprika or cracked black pepper on the crackers to complement the cheese.

125g (4oz) cream cheese
60g (2oz) strong Cheddar, very finely grated
1 tablespoon each of very finely chopped fresh chives, parsley, green shallots (spring onions)
1/2 teaspoon very finely chopped fresh lemon thyme
1 teaspoon Worcestershire sauce
cracked black peppercorns
finely chopped garlic
finely chopped chives

Blend all the ingredients, except for the chives, together very well. Spoon onto greased plastic wrap, form into a ball, wrap and refrigerate for at least 1 hour. Unwrap the cheese ball just before serving and roll in the chives.

Tofu and Herb Dip

1 cup (200g/7oz) mayonnaise
1 cup (240g/7 1/2oz) plain yoghurt
250g (8oz) soft tofu
1/2 teaspoon dill leaves
1/2 teaspoon dill seeds, crushed
1/2 teaspoon salt or herb salt
black pepper to taste
1 tablespoon finely chopped parsley
1 tablespoon finely chopped chives

Blend or process the mayonnaise, yoghurt, tofu, dill leaves and seeds, salt and pepper until well combined. Stir in the remaining ingredients and chill well.

Horseradish and Sesame Dip

There are many brands of nutritional yeast, some of which are very bitter. Choose one which suits your taste.

1 cup (200g/7oz) ricotta cheese
1/2 cup (75g/2 1/2oz) toasted sesame seeds, ground
1 tablespoon finely chopped parsley
1 tablespoon finely chopped chives
1 teaspoon finely chopped coriander leaves
1 tablespoon finely chopped onion
1 teaspoon lemon juice
1 tablespoon brewer's yeast flakes
1 tablespoon plain yoghurt
finely grated horseradish, to taste

Mix all the ingredients together, adjusting quantities to taste. Serve with crackers or vegetable sticks.

Lebanese Crackers

These crackers are quick and simple to make. They are a favourite in our family and I'm sure will become so in yours. Serve them with dips and as a crunchy and healthy snack for children.

Use any of the following toppings or a combination of 2 or more if you like.

wholemeal Lebanese pita breads
olive oil
powdered mixed herbs, paprika, onion salt, sesame seeds, cracked black pepper
chilli powder or anything else you can dream up

Split the breads in half. Brush the inside of each half lightly with olive oil. Sprinkle with the desired topping.

Press the topping firmly onto the bread with a spatula and cut each piece into 8 or more wedges, using scissors. Place the wedges in a single layer on baking trays and bake in a 180°C (350°F) until crisp and brown. These crackers store well in an airtight container for a few days but I don't imagine you will keep them for that long.

RIGHT: Horseradish and Sesame Dip

SOUPS

Pumpkin and Rosemary Soup

SERVES 4 TO 6

This soup can be made with any of the marrow or squash families. This version uses butternut pumpkin, a moist sweet flavoured pumpkin.

1 large butternut pumpkin
2 large onions, sliced
1 x 425g (14oz) can tomatoes, undrained
and chopped
14 rosemary leaves
vegetable stock
1/2 teaspoon ground nutmeg
salt and pepper to taste
1/2 cup (125ml/4fl oz) cream (double cream) or
plain yoghurt

Peel the pumpkin, cut in big chunks and place in a large saucepan. Add the onions, tomatoes, rosemary and enough stock to just cover the vegetables. Bring to the boil, cover and simmer until soft.

Stir in the remaining ingredients, purée the soup in a blender and reheat, but don't boil. Serve garnished with a few extra chopped rosemary leaves.

RIGHT: Pumpkin and Rosemary Soup (before puréeing)

Peanut and Nasturtium Soup

SERVES 4

This delicious thick soup can be thinned a little to taste with more stock. Serve sprinkled with chopped, toasted sunflower seeds or peanuts and decorate with a whole nasturtium flower.

1 large onion, chopped
1 stick celery, finely chopped
1 teaspoon aniseeds, crushed
1 clove garlic, crushed
2 tablespoons peanut oil
1 cup (180g/6oz) peanut butter
3 tablespoons low salt soy sauce,
1 cup (250ml/8fl oz) vegetable stock (or more, to taste)
1^1/$_2$ cups (375ml/12fl oz) hot milk
3–4 tablespoons plain yoghurt
3–4 tablespoons cream (heavy cream), optional
(increase plain yoghurt if preferred)
pinch cayenne pepper
3 nasturtium leaves, finely chopped

Sauté the onion, celery, aniseed and garlic in the peanut oil in a saucepan for 5 minutes.

Mix in the peanut butter, soy sauce and stock. Stir in the milk, a little at a time, until smooth and heat without boiling.

Combine the yoghurt, cream and cayenne, then stir into the peanut mixture.

Add the nasturtium leaves and reheat, if necessary, without boiling.

Golden Grain Soup

SERVES 4 TO 6

Don't be fooled by the conventional ingredients in this soup. It's unusual, delicious and healthy.

4 onions
3 tablespoons oil
^{1}/$_2$ teaspoon finely chopped oregano,
4 tablespoons finely chopped parsley
^{1}/$_2$ teaspoon finely chopped rosemary
1 teaspoon finely chopped basil

1 cup (90g/3oz) rolled oats
8 cups (2 litres/3^1/$_2$ pints) boiling water
3 tablespoons low salt soy sauce
salt and pepper to taste

Slice the onions into half moons and sauté in the oil in a saucepan on a low heat for about 10 minutes or until golden.

Add the herbs, oats and briskly boiling water (this is important or the oats will go 'gluggy'), then cook for 20–30 minutes, stirring occasionally.

Stir in the soy sauce, salt and pepper, then serve garnished with chopped herbs.

Six Herb Soup

SERVES 4

With the addition of croutons and grated cheese, this tasty soup makes a good lunch or a supper for a cold night.

2 onions, chopped
2 medium potatoes, cubed
1 large carrot, cubed
2 tablespoons Gourmet Garlic Oil
6 cups (1^1/$_2$ litres/2^1/$_2$ pints) well-flavoured stock
1 tablespoon finely chopped parsley
1 tablespoon finely chopped chives
2 teaspoons finely chopped rosemary
2 teaspoons finely chopped mint
2 teaspoons finely chopped savory
2 teaspoons finely chopped tarragon
salt and pepper to taste

Sauté the onions, potatoes and carrot gently in the garlic oil in a large saucepan for 5 minutes.

Add the stock and simmer for about 10 minutes or until the vegetables are half-cooked. Then add the herbs, setting some aside as a garnish, and simmer until completely cooked.

Serve with Herbed Croutons (see Treats and Tempters) and garnish with the remaining chopped fresh herbs.

RIGHT: Six Herb Soup

SALADS

Herb Salad

There is no formal recipe for this salad. I like to use two or more different types of lettuce, torn into smallish pieces. Then I add lots of landcress or watercress, alfalfa and red clover sprouts, chives, parsley, and very young dandelion leaves, torn into small bits. Now add smaller amounts of basil, dill or fennel leaves, lemon balm and nasturtium leaves and finish with just a little mint, oregano or marjoram and lemon thyme. Just before serving I toss the salad with Herb Vinaigrette. Garnish with any edible flowers.

Zucchini and Marjoram Salad

SERVES 4 TO 6

A very pretty salad which keeps for several days in the refrigerator. A delicious way to use zucchini (courgettes) in a glut!

2 medium zucchini (courgettes)
5 tablespoons chopped green shallots (spring onions)
1 red capsicum (pepper), sliced
1 green capsicum (pepper), sliced
2 tablespoons finely chopped parsley
1 tablespoon finely chopped marjoram
olives to garnish (optional)

DRESSING
1/2 cup (125ml/4fl oz) olive oil
3 tablespoons herb, cider or white wine vinegar
salt and black pepper to taste
2 teaspoons honey

Cut the zucchini (courgettes) into 1.5cm (1/2in) cubes, boil for 1 minute, strain and cool.

Add the green shallots (spring onions), capsicums (peppers), parsley and marjoram.

Make the dressing by combining all the ingredients in a screw-top jar. Shake well.

Toss the dressing through the zucchini mixture. Garnish with olives and herbs of your choice.

Green and Gold Salad

SERVES 4 TO 6

1 large carrot, sliced paper-thin
2 medium zucchini (courgettes), sliced paper-thin
2 tablespoons finely chopped green shallots (spring onions)
3 tablespoons finely chopped fresh mint
2 tablespoons finely chopped fresh parsley
1 teaspoon freshly ground black pepper
3 tablespoons olive oil
1 tablespoon lemon juice
salt to taste

Blanch the carrots in boiling water for 2 minutes and the zucchini (courgettes) for 1 minute; drain. Rinse in cold water, drain and cool.

Combine the green shallots (spring onions), herbs, pepper, oil, juice and salt in a bowl, then gently toss with the vegetables. Serve well chilled.

Roast Capsicum Salad

SERVES 4 TO 6

This versatile salad can be used in sandwiches, as a side dish with hot meals or together with other salads, to give flavour and colour. It keeps for several days in the refrigerator.

2 red capsicums (peppers)
2 green capsicums (peppers)
2 teaspoons Gourmet Garlic Oil
2 teaspoons lemon juice
salt and black pepper to taste

Bake the capsicums (peppers) in a baking dish in a 180°C (350°F) oven for about 30 minutes or until the skin begins to burn. Remove from the oven, cover with another dish and leave to cool.

Halve the capsicums, remove the stems and seeds, peel off the skin and slice the flesh into strips. Arrange decoratively in a bowl.

Combine the remaining ingredients and sprinkle over the capsicums.

RIGHT: Herb Salad

VEGETABLES

Potato Pancake

SERVES 4

1kg (2lb) potatoes
3 tablespoons oil
1 handful sprouts, finely chopped
4 green shallots (spring onions), finely chopped
1 tablespoon finely chopped tarragon
1 tablespoon finely chopped parsley
1 tablespoon finely chopped chives
salt and pepper to taste

Steam the potatoes until not quite cooked. Chill. Grate the cold potatoes into a bowl. Heat the oil in a heavy frying pan.

Add the remaining ingredients to the potatoes and mix gently. Spoon into the heated pan and cook until browned underneath. Turn and cook the other side. Cut into wedges to serve.

Cabbage or Carrots with Caraway

SERVES 4

Caraway serves a dual purpose in this recipe. It adds a subtle and interesting flavour and helps prevent the 'windy' discomfort experienced by many people after eating cabbage.

500g (1lb) cabbage or carrots, sliced
1 tablespoon oil
1 clove garlic, crushed
1 teaspoon caraway seeds, lightly crushed
$^{1}/_{2}$ cup (125ml/4fl oz) light sour cream (optional) or plain yoghurt

Steam the cabbage or carrots until tender but still crisp. Drain well and keep warm.

Heat the oil in a pan, add the garlic and caraway seeds and sauté for 2 minutes, then mix with the vegetable.

If using, fold through the sour cream or plain yoghurt and serve at once.

Bavarian Red Cabbage

SERVES 4

500g (1lb) red cabbage, shredded
1 onion, sliced
2 cloves garlic, crushed
2 tablespoons melted butter
1 cooking apple, chopped
1 bay leaf
1 teaspoon chopped parsley
1 teaspoon chopped oregano
1 teaspoon caraway seeds, crushed
pinch ground cinnamon
pinch ground nutmeg
salt and black pepper
2 teaspoons brown sugar
$^{1}/_{3}$ cup (80ml/2$^{1}/_{2}$fl oz) red wine
grated zest and juice of 1 orange

Sauté the cabbage, onion and garlic with the butter in a covered pan for 5–7 minutes.

Add the remaining ingredients, cover and cook gently for 20 minutes. Stir often and add a little more wine if too dry.

Tip

Add soft herbs such as basil and oregano towards the end of cooking time. Cooking these herbs for too long will result in their becoming quite bitter.

RIGHT: Bavarian Red Cabbage

Dilled Cucumbers

SERVES 4 TO 6

2 large cucumbers
1 tablespoon salt
1 onion, finely chopped
1 tablespoon butter
1 tablespoon plain flour
1¹/₂ cups (375ml/12fl oz) milk
1 tablespoon finely chopped parsley
1 tablespoon finely chopped fresh dill
1 tablespoon sour cream or plain yoghurt
salt and pepper to taste

Peel the cucumbers, cut lengthwise, remove the seeds and cut into 2.5cm (1in) pieces. Toss in the salt and leave to stand for an hour. Rinse and drain very well.

Sauté the onion in the butter until soft, then add the flour and cook, stirring, until light brown.

Remove from the heat and stir in the milk slowly. Stir until boiling and boil for 3–4 minutes, adding more milk if too thick.

Add the cucumbers and cook until tender but still firm.

Fold the herbs, yoghurt, salt and pepper through gently, garnish with extra chopped herbs and serve at once.

Sweet Corn and Capsicum Pancakes

SERVES 4

Use lemon thyme or either of the savories in this delicious recipe.

375g (12oz) sweet corn kernels
1 teaspoon lemon thyme or winter or summer savory, finely chopped
1 green capsicum (pepper), finely chopped
1 egg, separated
²/₃ cup (130g/4¹/₂oz) cornmeal (polenta)
¹/₃ cup (50g/1¹/₂oz) plain flour
salt and black pepper to taste
milk
oil to shallow-fry

Chop half the corn kernels finely and place with the remainder in a bowl.

Stir in the herb, capsicum (pepper), egg yolk, cornmeal (polenta), flour, salt and pepper, then mix with enough milk to form a soft dropping consistency.

Beat the egg white in a bowl until soft peaks form, then fold gently into the corn mixture. Drop a spoonful at a time into hot oil and cook on both sides until golden brown. Drain the pancakes well on paper towels before serving.

Cauliflower and Herb Combo

SERVES 4 TO 6

This delicious cauliflower dish can be served cold as a salad or warm as an accompaniment. If serving it as a salad, it helps to rinse the cooked cauliflower under cold water to stop the cooking process before tossing with the herb mixture.

1 small cauliflower
2 teaspoons finely chopped fresh parsley
1 teaspoon finely chopped fresh tarragon
1 teaspoon finely chopped fresh common chives or garlic chives
¹/₂ teaspoon finely chopped fresh lemon thyme
¹/₂ cup (125ml/4fl oz) mayonnaise
2 teaspoons lemon juice
cracked black peppercorns

Cut the cauliflower into very small florets. Steam for 2 minutes.

Combine all the remaining ingredients, then fold through the cauliflower. Serve warm or cold.

RIGHT: Sweet Corn and Capsicum Pancakes

SAUCES AND DRESSINGS

Herb Vinaigrette

MAKES ABOUT 125ML (4FL OZ)

The herbs in this dressing can be changed to suit the dish being served. The proportion of vinegar to oil may be changed to your own taste. If making this dressing ahead, add the herbs just before serving.

2 tablespoons white vinegar or lemon juice
1/3 cup (80ml/2 1/2fl oz) olive oil
2 teaspoons French mustard
1 clove garlic, crushed
2 teaspoons each of chopped chives,
parsley, basil
pinch sugar

Mix all the ingredients in a screw-top jar and shake really well.

Fresh Green Sauce

MAKES ABOUT 375ML (12FL OZ)

This sauce is delicious served over steaming hot vegetables or pasta. It can be made a day ahead.

1 cup (250ml/8fl oz) sour cream
60g (2oz) butter
1/8 teaspoon ground nutmeg
good pinch cayenne pepper
1/4 cup (30g/1oz) grated Parmesan cheese
1 tablespoon each of finely chopped basil,
parsley, mint, chives, tarragon, oregano and
lemon thyme

Combine the sour cream, butter, nutmeg and cayenne pepper in a saucepan and simmer for 3–5 minutes.

Beat the cheese and herbs into the sauce, then reheat and serve.

Basic Tomato Sauce

MAKES ABOUT 500ML (16FL OZ)

This basic sauce is the foundation for several sauces. It can be made in bulk and frozen in small amounts, ready to be converted into Mexican, Italian, Indian or herb sauce by adding the appropriate herbs and spices. To make a richer sauce, substitute red wine for some of the stock.

2 onions, chopped
2 cloves garlic, crushed
2 tablespoons olive oil
425g (14oz) can tomatoes, undrained
and chopped
1 cup (250ml/8fl oz) stock
2 tablespoons tomato paste
salt and pepper to taste

Sauté the onions and garlic in the olive oil until soft. Add the remaining ingredients and simmer, uncovered, until thickened.

Variations

Herb: Add 3 tablespoons finely chopped herbs of your choice.
Italian: Add 1 bay leaf before simmering and 1 tablespoon each of chopped basil and oregano before serving.
Indian: Sauté 1 tablespoon curry powder with the onions and garlic.
Mexican: Add cumin, fresh coriander and chilli to taste.

RIGHT: From top: Herb Vinaigrette, Basic Tomato Sauce, Fresh Green Sauce

Herb Mayonnaise

MAKES ABOUT 750ML (24FL OZ)

You can choose your favourite herbs for this creamy dressing. Fresh coriander is good, or a mixture of parsley, chives and landcress, or parsley and rosemary or basil.

2 eggs
2 tablespoons herb vinegar
1 tablespoon French mustard
pinch sugar
pinch salt and black pepper
2 cups (500ml/16fl oz) olive or safflower oil
$^1/_2$ cup (120g/about 4oz) plain yoghurt
1 cup (30g/1oz) very finely chopped fresh herbs
of your choice

Blend the eggs, vinegar, mustard, sugar, salt and pepper together in a blender or food processor. With the motor running, dribble in the oil very slowly, until really thick.

Stir in the plain yoghurt, adjust seasoning to taste and finally stir in the fresh herbs.

Potato Salad Dressing

MAKES ABOUT 125ML (4FL OZ)

This easy dressing can be tossed through hot cooked potato pieces or baby new potatoes. For a sweeter flavour, use sweet potato.

2 tablespoons olive oil
2 tablespoons white wine vinegar
1 onion, finely chopped
1 tablespoon finely chopped fresh parsley
2 teaspoons finely chopped fresh chives
1 teaspoon finely chopped fresh mint or dill
cracked black peppercorns
salt (optional)

Combine all the ingredients in a screw-top jar, cover and shake thoroughly to combine the flavours. Toss through hot or cold cooked whole or quartered potatoes.

Green Dressing

MAKES ABOUT 250ML (8FL OZ)

This dressing is delicious over all types of salads and hot vegetables.

100g (3$^1/_2$oz) English spinach leaves
1 clove garlic
2 tablespoons green shallots (spring onions),
chopped
$^1/_2$ cup (125ml/4fl oz) mayonnaise
1 tablespoon fresh dill
$^1/_2$ teaspoon chopped tarragon
3 tablespoons chopped parsley
$^1/_2$ cup (120g/about 4oz) plain yoghurt
2 tablespoons lemon juice (or less to taste)
salt and black pepper to taste

Tear the spinach into small pieces, blanch 1 minute in boiling water, drain, squeeze dry and leave to cool.

Blend the spinach with the remaining ingredients in a blender or food processor until very smooth.

Neil's Sauce

MAKES ABOUT 375ML (12FL OZ)

This high cholesterol but delicious dressing, a personal favourite from award-winning Australian chef Neil Jackson, is a treat for special occasions. You can substitute red wine vinegar for white to make a more robust sauce or use orange juice in place of lemon. Serve with vegetables of all kinds.

1$^1/_2$ tablespoons white wine
1$^1/_2$ tablespoons white wine vinegar
1 tablespoon chopped onion
300g (10oz) butter
1 teaspoon lemon juice
salt and pepper to taste

Simmer the wine, vinegar and onion together in a small saucepan until the liquid has almost evaporated. Whisk in the butter and lemon juice, then add salt and pepper to taste.

RIGHT: Herb Mayonnaise

ENTREES AND MAIN COURSES

Mushroom Pâté

SERVES 6 AS AN ENTREE

³/₄ cup (90g/3oz) finely chopped green shallots
(spring onions)
1 tablespoon melted butter
500g (1lb) mushrooms, finely chopped
1 stick celery, finely chopped
3 tablespoons finely chopped parsley
¹/₄ teaspoon each of finely chopped basil,
oregano, sage and rosemary
2 eggs, lightly beaten
1 cup (125g/4oz) grated cheddar cheese
¹/₂ cup (50g/1 ¹/₂oz) dry, fine breadcrumbs
salt and black pepper to taste
1 tablespoon brandy
60g (2oz) extra butter, melted

Preheat the oven to 180°C (350°F).

Sauté the spring onions in the melted butter for 5 minutes. Remove from heat and combine with the mushrooms, celery, herbs, eggs, cheese, breadcrumbs, salt, pepper and brandy.

Spoon the mixture into a small greased loaf pan. Pour the extra melted butter over, cover and bake for 1 hour. Cool before serving.

Herbed Camembert Parcels

SERVES 4

4 sheets fillo pastry
melted butter
1 x 220g (7oz) whole camembert cheese
1 teaspoon finely chopped basil
¹/₂ teaspoon paprika
1 egg, beaten

Preheat the oven to 200°C (400°F).

Brush each pastry sheet with melted butter and fold in half lengthwise. Cut the cheese into 4 wedges. Place 1 wedge on the end of each strip of pastry. Sprinkle the basil and paprika over each cheese wedge, then fold a corner of pastry over to enclose the cheese into a triangle shape, continue folding until the strip is used up, sealing the final edge with beaten egg.

Brush the tops of the parcels with egg, place on a greased baking tray and bake for about 15 minutes or until browned. Serve with slices of tomato and basil leaves to decorate.

Italian Fish Fillets

SERVES 3 TO 6

This recipe can be made with your choice of herbs but it is delicious with basil, marjoram and parsley, or parsley, chives and a pinch of rosemary.

6 fillets of white fish
1–2 tablespoons butter, softened
salt and pepper
2 teaspoons selected finely chopped fresh herbs
juice of 1 lemon
¹/₂ cup (125ml/4fl oz) white wine

Arrange the fish fillets in a shallow ovenproof dish. Combine the butter, salt and pepper and 1 teaspoon of the herbs, and spread over the fish.

Pour the combined lemon juice and wine over the fish and bake in a 180°C (350°F) oven for 10 minutes or until the fish is cooked in the middle.

Lift the fish onto a serving plate and keep warm. Pour the juices into a small pan, add the remaining herbs and boil to reduce a little. Pour over the fish and serve immediately.

RIGHT: Italian Fish Fillets

Sage and Savory Sausages

SERVES 3 TO 4

2 eggs, beaten
2 tablespoons peanut butter
100g (4oz) cottage cheese
1 cup (125g/4oz) grated Cheddar cheese
1/2 cup (75g/2 1/2oz) chopped mixed nuts
1 onion, finely chopped
1/2 teaspoon each of finely chopped sage and
winter savory
1 teaspoon French mustard
1/2 teaspoon salt
1 teaspoon curry powder
about 100g (4oz) fine, fresh breadcrumbs
1 egg white, lightly beaten
fine dry breadcrumbs
oil for shallow-frying

Combine the eggs, peanut butter, cheeses, nuts, onion, herbs, mustard, salt, curry powder and fresh breadcrumbs in a bowl and mix well. Adjust the amount of fresh breadcrumbs if necessary to make a soft but 'mouldable' texture. Shape into sausages, place on a tray and leave in the refrigerator for an hour to set.

Dip the sausages into beaten egg white and then dry breadcrumbs to coat. Fry the sausages in hot oil until golden brown.

Coconut Chicken with Lemon Grass

SERVES 4 TO 6

1 1/2kg (3lb) chicken pieces
1 tablespoon oil
5 cloves garlic, crushed
2 onions, chopped
1 small red and 1 small green capsicum
(pepper), chopped
250g (8oz) drained, canned tomatoes
2 teaspoons turmeric
3 tablespoons chopped fresh coriander
1/2 teaspoon fennel seeds, ground
1 teaspoon ground cumin
2 cups (500ml/16fl oz) coconut milk

1 tablespoon cornflour
1 teaspoon grated fresh ginger
1/2 teaspoon chilli powder
2 bay leaves
1 teaspoon coconut, toasted
2 lemon grass stalks
1 cinnamon stick

Fry the chicken pieces in the oil in a frying pan until golden brown, then drain well. In the same pan, sauté 3 of the cloves of garlic with the onions and capsicums (peppers), then remove and drain well. Arrange the chicken in a baking dish, and top with the capsicum mixture.

Purée the remaining garlic with the tomatoes, turmeric, coriander, fennel, cumin, coconut milk, cornflour, ginger and chilli powder in a blender or food processor and pour over the chicken and vegetables.

Stir in the remaining ingredients and cook in a 180°C (350°F) oven for about 50 minutes or until the chicken is cooked. Remove the bay leaves, lemon grass and cinnamon before serving.

Italian Chicken and Spaghetti

SERVES 4 TO 6

1 onion, finely chopped
2 cloves garlic, crushed
3 tablespoons olive oil
1 1/2kg (3lb) chicken pieces
2 1/2 cups (625ml/20fl oz) Basic Tomato Sauce –
Italian variation
3 tablespoons finely chopped parsley

Sauté the onion and garlic in the oil, then add the chicken and cook until browned all over.

Pour the tomato sauce over the chicken, cover the pan and simmer for about 30 minutes or until the chicken is tender. If too dry, add a little stock or water. Remove the chicken to a warm dish and add 1 or 2 tablespoons parsley to the sauce.

Boil spaghetti for 4–6 people, place in hot dish and arrange the chicken on top. Cover with the sauce and sprinkle with the remaining parsley.

RIGHT: Coconut Chicken with Lemon Grass

Nasturtium Kebabs

SERVES 4

500g (1lb) chicken breast fillets, cubed
1/3 cup (80ml/2 1/2fl oz) Herb Vinegar
1/3 cup (80ml/2 1/2fl oz) Gourmet Garlic Oil
1 tablespoon soy sauce
1 teaspoon crushed fresh ginger
1 tablespoon sherry
24 button mushrooms
24 cherry tomatoes
1 green and 1 red pepper (capsicum), chopped
12 pickling onions
2 tablespoons chopped chives
8 nasturtium flowers, chopped
Pickled Nasturtium Seeds, chopped
3/4 cup (180g/about 6oz) plain yoghurt
salt and pepper to taste
nasturtium leaves

Marinate the chicken in a glass dish overnight in the combined herb vinegar, garlic oil, soy sauce, ginger and sherry.

Drain the chicken and reserve the marinade. Thread the chicken and vegetables alternately onto 8 skewers. Grill or barbecue the kebabs, brushing with the reserved marinade, until cooked through.

Combine the chives, nasturtium flowers and seeds then mix with the plain yoghurt and salt and pepper to make a dressing.

Remove the kebabs from the skewers and serve on the nasturtium leaves. Top with the dressing, then roll up and eat.

Herbed Eggplant

SERVES 4 AS A SIDE DISH

1 medium eggplant (aubergine)
salt
2 tablespoons Gourmet Garlic Oil
1 tablespoon crushed fresh ginger
1 clove crushed garlic
2 tablespoons chopped chives
1 tablespoon finely chopped onion
1 tablespoon chopped parsley
2 tablespoons chopped mint
juice of 1 lemon
1/2 cup (125ml/4fl oz) sour cream
2 tablespoons plain yoghurt

Cut the eggplant (aubergine) into cubes, toss in salt and leave to sweat in a colander for 1 hour. Rinse thoroughly and pat dry, then sauté with the oil, ginger and garlic for about 6 minutes.

Combine the remaining ingredients and fold through the eggplant mixture. Serve the herbed eggplant hot or well chilled.

Cheese and Eggplant Balls

SERVES 4

You can vary this dish to suit your mood. Use coriander for a Mexican dish and oregano for an Italian-style flavour.

1 medium eggplant (aubergine)
salt
2 eggs, beaten
3 tablespoons grated Cheddar cheese
2 tablespoons finely chopped parsley
2 tablespoons ground almonds
2 tablespoons chopped coriander or oregano
oil for shallow-frying
3 cups (750ml/25fl oz) Basic Tomato Sauce
salt and pepper (optional)

Grate the eggplant (aubergine) and toss it with salt. Leave it to sweat in a colander for 1 hour, then rinse thoroughly and squeeze really dry.

Combine the eggs, cheese, parsley, almonds and half the coriander or oregano. Add the eggplant and mix well. Shape the mixture into small balls and shallow-fry in hot oil until golden brown. Drain on paper towels.

Add the remaining coriander or oregano to the sauce with salt and pepper to taste. Pour half the Basic Tomato Sauce into an ovenproof dish. Add the eggplant balls and pour over the remaining sauce.

Bake in a 180°C (350°F) oven for 30 minutes. Serve while hot.

RIGHT: From top: Nasturtium Kebabs, Herbed Eggplant

DESSERTS

Lemon Balm and Mint Fruit Salad

Choose enough fruit in season for the amount of salad you want to make, paying attention to colour combinations and texture. A mixture of soft and crunchy is pleasing to the tongue and teeth. Eye appeal is important too. Pineapple, kiwi fruit, apples and a few red plums are good together, or try melon, kiwi fruit and strawberries.

For a fresh fruit salad, try making juice from 2 parts fresh orange juice and 1 part fresh lemon juice, then sweetening to taste with honey or sugar. Add finely chopped lemon balm and mint leaves for a really zippy flavour.

Mango Magic

SERVES 4

To save grating the ginger, try using Ginger Honey instead of honey and fresh ginger.

3 large, ripe mangoes
2 tablespoons honey
1 teaspoon finely grated fresh ginger
juice of 1 lemon
1 tablespoon finely chopped lemon balm
1 teaspoon finely chopped mint

Peel and cube the mangoes and place in a dish.

Warm the honey in a saucepan until runny, stir in the ginger. Add the lemon juice and herbs then pour over the mangoes. Chill before serving.

Tip

Be adventurous with food garnishes: dandelion flower petals, calendula petals on green soups; the feathery fronds and golden flowers of fennel on fish; rose petals on a pale pink dessert. Use your imagination and create food that looks as good as it tastes.

Angel Custard

SERVES 4

3 angelica stalks
2³/₄ cups (680ml/22fl oz) milk
3 tablespoons Ginger Honey
4 eggs, lightly beaten
1 tablespoon melted butter

Peel and cut the angelica into very thin rings.

Combine the milk and Ginger Honey in a saucepan, bring to a boil then add the angelica. Remove from the heat, cover and stand for at least 2 hours.

Preheat the oven to 120°C (240°F). Reheat the milk mixture until lukewarm and stir in the eggs, then butter. Pour into an ovenproof dish and bake on the middle shelf of the oven until just set in the centre (don't overcook). Serve hot or cold.

Herbed Dessert Cheese

1kg (2lb) plain yoghurt
¹/₃ cup (20g/²/₃oz) finely chopped fresh lemon balm or mint
1 tablespoon grated orange or lemon zest

Combine the yoghurt, herb and zest together and mix well. Place in a double cheesecloth or muslin bag or a boiled tea towel. Tie the ends together and allow to hang over a bowl and drip overnight.

To serve, remove the cheese from the bag, pat into shape. Decorate with fresh herb leaves and serve with fresh fruit.

RIGHT: Lemon Balm and Mint Fruit Salad

Mint Sorbet

SERVES 4 TO 6

1½ cups (330g/11oz) sugar
2 cups (500ml/16fl oz) water
2 teaspoons mint, crushed to a pulp
1 teaspoon each lemon thyme and lemon balm,
crushed to a pulp
juice of 3 lemons, strained
1 egg white

Combine the sugar and water in a saucepan, stir over a low heat until the sugar is dissolved. Simmer for 5 minutes, add the herbs and cool.

Add the lemon juice, then freeze in a shallow container until firm around the edges.

Scrape the mixture into a bowl and whisk, then gently fold in the stiffly beaten egg white. Pour back into the container and refreeze. Serve in chilled glass dishes decorated with herb leaves.

Caramel Herb Oranges

SERVES 4 TO 6

You can choose your favourite herbs for this recipe but mint and lemon thyme are very good.

6 large oranges, peeled, with all white
pith removed
2 teaspoons finely chopped herbs
1 teaspoon caster sugar
1 tablespoon Cointreau
½ cup (110g/3½oz) sugar
⅓ cup (80ml/2½fl oz) water

Cut the oranges into thin slices and arrange on a dish. Sprinkle with the herbs, caster sugar and Cointreau.

Combine the sugar and water in a saucepan and heat gently while stirring until the sugar is dissolved. Simmer, uncovered, until golden brown but don't overcook. Pour over the oranges and chill for several hours before serving.

Angelic Pie

SERVES 4 TO 6

5 medium cooking apples, peeled, cored and
thinly sliced
5 tablespoons raw sugar
2 tablespoons finely chopped angelica stalk
½ teaspoon finely chopped lemon thyme
⅔ cup (160ml/5½fl oz) white wine
1 or 2 x 25cm (10in) square sheets prepared
shortcrust pastry
2 tablespoons plain flour
cream (double cream) or plain yoghurt

Toss the apple slices with the sugar and layer with the herbs in an ovenproof dish.

Pour the wine over, cover and bake in a 135°C (275°F) oven for 1–2 hours or until the apples are very tender. Cool thoroughly.

Line a pie dish with the pastry, and bake blind for 15 minutes in a 190°C (375°F) oven.

Fold the flour through the apple mixture and pour into the cooked pie shell. Cover with the cream or plain yoghurt or a mixture of both and continue baking for 40 minutes.

Southernwood Cake

Nirala, my good friend, gave me the recipe for this unlikely sounding but lovely cake.

4 eggs, lightly beaten
185g (6oz) butter, melted and cooled
1½ cups (225g/7oz) self-raising flour
½ cup (75g/2½oz) plain flour
1 cup (220g/7½oz) sugar
1 tablespoon very finely chopped
southernwood leaves
2 teaspoons caraway seeds
1 teaspoon grated lemon zest

Pre-heat the oven to 180°C (350°F). Grease a 25cm (10in) square cake pan and line the base.

Combine the eggs and melted butter. Fold in the sifted flours and sugar, then the remaining ingredients. Spoon the mixture into the cake pan. Bake for about 45 minutes or until cooked.

RIGHT: Angelic Pie

CONDIMENTS

Dill Pickles

4 cups (1 litre/1³/₄ pints) cider vinegar
2 cups (500ml/16fl oz) water
¹/₂ cup (110g/3¹/₂oz) salt
gherkins or small cucumbers
3 cloves garlic
3 bay leaves
3 tablespoons dill seeds
1 tablespoon mixed pickling spice

Combine the vinegar, water and salt in a non-aluminium saucepan, bring to a boil, then cool. Layer the remaining ingredients in a wide-mouthed jar or crock and pour the brine over.

Cover and leave at least a week before using. You can add more gherkins to the pot as it empties.

Tip

Keep a small, decorative pot of fennel seeds on the dining table and nibble a few seeds at the end of each meal. Fennel will ensure sweet breath and help to digest fats.

Coriander, Mint and Coconut Chutney, Spread or Dip

If you like fresh coriander and peanuts, you will love this dish. It can be used as a chutney or a spread or dip, or served over rice, with curry dishes, baked fish or patties.

1 cup (90g/3oz) coconut
³/₄ cup (110g/3¹/₂oz) raw, unsalted peanuts
4 tablespoons chopped coriander
5 sprigs mint leaves, chopped
¹/₈ teaspoon chilli powder
1 tablespoon grated fresh ginger
2 tablespoons lemon juice
1 cup (240g/about 8oz) plain yoghurt
1 teaspoon sugar
salt to taste

Blend or process all the ingredients together, leaving the nuts coarsely chopped. Add more plain yoghurt if the mixture is too dry.

Horseradish Sauce

Serve this sauce with meat, poultry or fish, and even vegetables.

60g (2oz) horseradish root, finely grated
¹/₂ teaspoon dry mustard
2 teaspoons sugar
cider vinegar to cover
¹/₂–1 cup (125–250ml/4–8fl oz) thickened cream (double cream)
salt and pepper

Combine the horseradish, mustard and sugar in a bowl, pour the vinegar over the mixture, and leave overnight.

Fold in the cream and adjust seasoning to taste. Store in a covered jar in refrigerator.

RIGHT: Coriander, Mint and Coconut Chutney, Spread or Dip

Pickled Nasturtium Seeds

I use these instead of capers. They are much tastier and better textured.

fresh nasturtium seeds
1$\frac{1}{2}$ tablespoons salt
1$\frac{1}{2}$ cups (375ml/12fl oz) water
white wine vinegar or cider vinegar

Place the seeds in a bowl or jar. Combine the salt and water then pour enough over the seeds to cover. Stand overnight.

Drain the seeds, then pour over enough salt solution to cover. Stand overnight.

Repeat this once more, allowing the seeds to stand a third night. Drain and rinse the seeds well, place in a sterilised jar and cover with the vinegar. Leave for 5–6 weeks before using.

The Very Best Tomato Ketchup

2kg (4lb) very ripe tomatoes, peeled and chopped
3 teaspoons allspice
2 tablespoons mustard seeds
3 medium onions, finely chopped
3 cloves garlic, crushed
1 cup (220g/7$\frac{1}{2}$oz) sugar
3 tablespoons finely chopped basil
1 tablespoon finely chopped oregano
1 tablespoon finely chopped lemon thyme
2 cups (500ml/16fl oz) cider vinegar
$\frac{1}{2}$ teaspoon ground black pepper

Place the tomatoes in a non-aluminium pan. Tie the allspice and mustard seeds in a muslin bag. Add to the tomatoes.

Add the onions and garlic and simmer, uncovered, stirring often, for about 30 minutes or until thickened and reduced.

Stir in the remaining ingredients and continue simmering, uncovered, until the mixture reaches a sauce consistency. Pour into hot sterilised bottles and seal while still hot.

Grainy and Gorgeous Mustard

This coarse-textured mustard owes some of its delicious, mild flavour to green peppercorns. If you prefer your mustard hotter, you can use black peppercorns. All mustards need to be matured for about two weeks before use, as they taste acrid until the flavours have blended.

4 tablespoons mixed mustard seeds
1 tablespoon green or black peppercorns
2 tablespoons red wine
$\frac{2}{3}$ cup (160ml/5$\frac{1}{2}$fl oz) red wine vinegar
3 cloves garlic, crushed
1 bay leaf, finely chopped
$\frac{1}{2}$ teaspoon Worcestershire sauce
1 teaspoon honey
$\frac{1}{4}$ cup (60ml/2fl oz) water

Blend the mustard seeds and peppercorns to a coarse texture in a blender or coffee grinder, then mix with the remaining ingredients.

Soak for 2 hours, then put into a small saucepan and cook, stirring continuously for 5–10 minutes. Add more vinegar if too dry.

Spoon into a sterilised jar and seal well. Keep refrigerated.

RIGHT: The Very Best Tomato Ketchup

HERB VINEGARS

It's important to use only a very good quality vinegar. Cheap vinegars are harsh and they completely overpower the flavour of the herbs. The method is the same for all types:

Heat the vinegar but don't boil. Pour over the whole herbs (don't chop them unless specified), leave for one week, strain and bottle. You can top up with fresh herbs and vinegar as needed. Here are some good combinations.

Basil Garlic Vinegar

MAKES ABOUT 500ML (16FL OZ)

4 tablespoons chopped basil
3 cloves garlic, quartered
2 cups (500ml/16fl oz) cider or white wine vinegar

Ginger Coconut Vinegar

MAKES ABOUT 250ML (8FL OZ)

1 tablespoon chopped fresh ginger
1 cup (250ml/8fl oz) coconut vinegar

Mixed Herb Vinegar

MAKES ABOUT 375ML (12FL OZ)

10 stalks chives, chopped
1 sprig of dill
2 sprigs of thyme
6 leaves oregano
1$\frac{1}{2}$ cups (375ml/12fl oz) white or cider vinegar

Orange or Lemon Mint Vinegar

MAKES ABOUT 500ML (16FL OZ)

2 strips orange or lemon rind without white pith, about 2.5cm (1in) long
12 peppermint or apple mint leaves
2 cups (500ml/16fl oz) white wine vinegar

Raspberry Vinegar

MAKES ABOUT 750ML (24FL OZ)

500g (1lb) raspberries
2 tablespoons honey
2 cups (500ml/16fl oz) red wine vinegar

Mash the raspberries and place in a large jar, then mix in the honey.

Heat the vinegar, then pour it over the raspberries. Cover and stand for 2 days.

Strain through a doubled cheesecloth, then through a coffee filter paper. Pour into a sterilised bottle.

Gourmet Vinegar

MAKES ABOUT 750ML (24FL OZ)

3 cups (750ml/1$\frac{1}{4}$pints) white wine vinegar
1 tablespoon grated horseradish root
2 green shallots (spring onions), finely chopped
2 sprigs each of rosemary and thyme
2 teaspoons chopped tarragon
grated zest and juice of 1 lemon

Heat the vinegar without boiling. Combine the remaining ingredients in a sterilised jar and pour the vinegar over.

Cover and leave one week, then strain well and bottle.

RIGHT: From left: Raspberry Vinegar, Mixed Herb Vinegar, Gourmet Vinegar

FLAVOURED OILS

Gourmet Garlic Oil

This takes only minutes to prepare, tastes delicious and will save you a lot of time if you use garlic often.

Three-quarters fill a reasonably wide-necked bottle with gently warmed, best quality, extra virgin olive oil. Add 3–8 cloves of garlic cut in half. The number of cloves depends on the size of your bottle and how strong you want the oil to be.

The oil will be ready to use the next day but will become stronger as the days pass. Keep topping up the bottle as needed. After about 4 weeks, remove the garlic and add fresh ones.

Variation

This method can also be used for herbs such as basil, tarragon and oregano, the oil is useful for dressings or for cooking. Crush the herbs lightly before adding to the oil.

Herb Oil

It's best to make small quantities of this oil to make sure it keeps fresh. I would use about 2 cups (500ml/16fl oz) of combined oils.

$^{1}/_{2}$ cup (15g/$^{1}/_{2}$oz) chopped fresh tarragon
$^{1}/_{4}$ cup (7g/$^{1}/_{4}$oz) fresh thyme leaves
$^{1}/_{4}$ cup (7g/$^{1}/_{4}$oz) chopped fresh chives
2 teaspoons crushed celery seed
olive oil
safflower oil

Place the herbs into a clean jar. It should be only half-filled. Fill the jar with a mixture of the olive oil and safflower oil. Cover.

Leave the jar in a warm place for two weeks, shaking the jar often. Strain and then re-bottle. If giving as a gift, add several pink and green peppercorns to each bottle.

Hot Chilli Oil

Don't treat this oil lightly – it's a good servant but a cruel master! If sautéeing, mix it with some plain oil. Add in very small quantities to dips, dressings, bastes and marinades.

2 cups (500ml/16fl oz) safflower oil
$^{1}/_{2}$ cup (15g/$^{1}/_{2}$oz) dried chillies, chopped
1 teaspoon chilli powder
$^{1}/_{4}$ cup (50g/$1^{1}/_{2}$oz) chopped fresh ginger
24 black peppercorns, bruised
6 cloves garlic, crushed
1 medium onion, chopped

Warm the oil. Add all the remaining ingredients and stand overnight. Strain the oil through double cheesecloth. Pour into a large clean bottle. Seal well. If giving as a gift, add 1 red chilli to each bottle.

Asian-style Chilli Oil

A simpler oil for those who like a milder chilli flavour with a definite Asian flavour. Removing the seeds from the chillies makes the oil even milder as the seeds are the hottest part of the chillies. This oil will keep for about 3 months.

2 green chillies
1 red chilli
$^{1}/_{4}$ cup (7g/$^{1}/_{4}$oz) coriander leaves
2 tablespoons chopped lemon grass
2 cups safflower oil or light olive oil
1 teaspoon chilli powder
2 strips lime rind

Cut the chillies in half and remove the seeds if you wish. Place the chillies in a large, screw-topped jar.

Warm the oil and pour over the chillies. Add all the remaining ingredients and mix well. Stand for 2 days then strain through double cheesecloth and pour into a large clean bottle. If giving as a gift, add 1 green and 1 red chilli to each bottle.

RIGHT: From left: Gourmet Garlic Oil, Hot Chilli Oil, Herb Oil, Asian-style Chilli Oil

TREATS AND TEMPERS

Preserved Angelica Stem

I have tried lots of methods and find this old recipe to be the best. It's worth a bit of a bother.

Cut young angelica stems into 5cm (2in) lengths and boil until tender. Remove from the water and peel. Return to the water and simmer gently until very green.

Drain, cool, then weigh. Allow an equal weight of sugar to angelica. Sprinkle the sugar over and leave for 2–3 days. Bring to the boil, simmer for 10 minutes, drain, spread over a wire rack over a baking tray. Place in a cool oven to dry.

Frosted Leaves and Flowers

This method can be used for any leaves or flowers you would like to use as garnishes. They will store for a short time between layers of greaseproof paper in an airtight tin.

Beat an egg white with a pinch of salt until just broken down (don't overbeat). Brush (don't dip) leaves and flowers very lightly with egg white, using a fairly fine paint brush. Sprinkle with caster sugar and place on greaseproof paper. Set the oven to its lowest heat and dry the leaves and flowers on the bottom shelf, leaving the door open, for 20–30 minutes.

Herb Croutons

These are great in salads, soups and stews. Make a pile and store in an airtight container.

Cut cubes of bread from an unsliced wholemeal loaf and drizzle with Gourmet Garlic Oil. Chop a heap of mixed herbs and toss through the bread cubes, add salt and pepper to taste and place the cubes in a single layer on baking trays. Bake in a 180°C (350°F) oven for about 10 minutes or until very crunchy.

Savoury Pikelets

$^1/_2$ cup (125ml/4fl oz) milk
$^1/_2$ cup (120g/about 4oz) plain yoghurt
1 egg
$^1/_2$ cup (75g/2$^1/_2$oz) self-raising flour
pinch bicarbonate of soda
1 tablespoon finely chopped herbs
2 tablespoons grated Parmesan cheese
pinch each of paprika and salt

Blend the milk, yoghurt and egg, and stand for 5–10 minutes.

Add the remaining ingredients and blend to a thick batter, adding more milk if needed.

Spoon tablespoons of batter onto a heated greased frying pan or griddle. Cook until browned underneath, turn and cook on the other side until browned.

Summer Cookies

This is another recipe from my friend Nirala. If using rose petals, use dried, heavily scented ones. Cut the white bit from the base as it is bitter.

125g (4oz) butter
$^3/_4$ cup (165g/5$^1/_2$oz) sugar
4 heads lavender flowers or 2 tablespoons rose petals
$^1/_4$ cup (60g/2oz) sugar, extra
2 eggs, lightly beaten
$^1/_2$ teaspoon vanilla essence or rosewater
1$^1/_2$ cups (225g/7$^1/_2$oz) self-raising flour

Pre-heat the oven to 180°C (350°F).

Cream the butter and sugar until light and fluffy. Grind the flowers or petals with the extra sugar until very fine and add to the butter mixture. Add the beaten eggs and the flavouring. Fold in the sifted flour.

Place teaspoons of mixture on an ungreased baking tray and flatten slightly. Bake for about 8 minutes or until golden brown. Cool slightly on the tray and then transfer to a wire cooling rack.

RIGHT: Frosted leaves and flowers beautifully decorate a cake and biscuits

Preserved Ginger

1kg (2lb) fresh ginger
1 rounded teaspoon bicarbonate of soda
4 cups (880g/30oz) white sugar
1 cup (250ml/8fl oz) water

Wash and scrape the skin from the ginger. Cut the ginger into 0.5cm (^{1}/4in) cubes. Cover with water in a non-aluminium pan, bring to a boil and simmer for 10 minutes. Drain.

Add the bicarbonate of soda, cover again with water and boil for 20 minutes. Drain, then repeat boiling for about 30–45 minutes or until the ginger is tender.

Combine half the sugar with the water in a saucepan, stir over a low heat until the sugar is dissolved. Simmer gently for 5 minutes, then add the ginger. Cover and simmer for 10 minutes. Pour into a dish, cover and leave for 2–3 days. Strain the syrup into a saucepan.

Add 1 cup of the remaining sugar to the syrup, stir over a low heat until the sugar is dissolved and simmer gently for 5 minutes.

Pour over the ginger and leave for 24 hours. Strain and repeat this process with the remaining cup of sugar and the syrup.

Cheese and Herb Biscuits

^{1}/3 cup (45g/1^1/2oz) grated tasty cheese
^{1}/3 cup (50g/1^1/2oz) self-raising flour
80g (2^1/2oz) butter, melted
1–2 teaspoons finely chopped herbs,
pinch each of salt and cayenne
coconut, toasted

Preheat the oven to 180°C (350°F).

Combine the cheese, flour, butter, herbs, salt and cayenne in a bowl, mix thoroughly and roll into small balls.

Roll the balls in the coconut and flatten slightly. Place onto lightly greased baking trays. Bake for about 15 minutes or until lightly browned. Cool on the trays.

Cottage Cheese with Herbs

You can add finely chopped capsicums (peppers), gherkins, green shallots (spring onions) or anything you like to this cheese. It's very easy to make but be gentle with it or it might be tough. Make it in a non-aluminium pan. Serve as a dip, on sandwiches or with salad.

2 tablespoons lemon juice
2 tablespoons warm water
4 cups (1 litre/1^3/4 pints) skim or whole milk
1–2 tablespoons very finely chopped herbs
salt and black pepper

Combine the lemon juice and water.

Heat the milk to boiling point, remove from the heat and slowly drizzle in the lemon mixture, stirring very gently. Stop stirring and adding when the curds separate and the whey is yellowish and clear. Leave for 1 hour. With a slotted spoon, gently lift the curds into a bowl.

Fold the herbs gently into the cheese, add salt and black pepper to taste and spoon into a cheesecloth-lined sieve or colander. Leave to drain for 1–2 hours, or hang in the cheesecloth as shown in the photograph.

Herb Stuffing for Roast Chicken

2 tablespoons chopped parsley
2 teaspoons chopped lemon thyme
1 teaspoon grated lemon zest
salt and pepper to taste
1 egg, beaten
^{1}/2 cup (40g/1^1/2oz) fine, fresh breadcrumbs

Combine the herbs, zest, salt and pepper and leave for about 1 hour for the flavours to mature.

Stir in the egg, then enough breadcrumbs to make a moist but firm consistency.

RIGHT: From left: Cottage Cheese with Herbs, Cheese and Herb Biscuits

FLAVOURING WITH HERBS

Roast Chicken Rub

1 clove garlic, crushed
½ teaspoon dried, ground thyme
½ teaspoon salt
pepper to taste
2 teaspoons paprika
½ teaspoon dried ground tarragon
2 tablespoons oil

Combine all the ingredients in a bowl. Rub the mixture over the chicken and stand for 30 minutes before baking.

Herb Salt

You can boost the vitamin B content of this recipe by adding 6 tablespoons mild brewer's yeast flakes, crushed. Some yeasts are very bitter so choose your brand carefully.

1½ cups (225g/7½oz) roast, ground sesame seeds
½ cup (60g/2oz) dried, ground celery tops
2 teaspoons dried, ground garlic
1 teaspoon dried, ground dill seed
4 cups (500g/1lb) dried, ground parsley
2 teaspoons dried, ground oregano
2 teaspoons dried, ground lemon thyme
2 teaspoons dried, ground coriander
2 teaspoons ground paprika

Combine all the ingredients well, pass through a fine sieve and store most of the mix in the freezer. Keep out enough for table and cooking use.

DRIED OR FRESH HERB BLENDS

Most of the herbs in these varieties are either dried and crumbled (not ground) or fresh. Add the herbs towards the end of cooking time.

Fines Herbes

2 parts parsley, 4 parts chives, 1 part celery tops, 1 part thyme,

Omelette Herbs

3 parts parsley, 2 parts chives, 1 part dill, 1 part tarragon

For Soups and Stews

4 parts parsley, 4 parts chives, 2 parts bay leaves
2 parts thyme, 1 part lemon thyme, 2 parts garlic

For Tomato Dishes

4 parts oregano, 8 parts basil, 2 parts lemon thyme, 1 part garlic

For Meat Dishes

2 parts parsley, 4 parts chives, 2 parts marjoram, 1 part thyme, 1 part celery tops, 1 part garlic

Herbs for Poultry Casseroles

2 parts parsley, 4 parts chives, 1 part tarragon, 2 parts celery tops

For Fish

8 parts parsley, 2 parts hyssop, 2 parts fennel, 1 part oregano, 1 part lemon thyme

General Bouquet

2 parts parsley, 4 parts chives, 1 part oregano, 1 part tarragon, 1 part thyme, 1 part sage

Salad Herbs

4 parts borage, 2 parts chives, 2 parts dill, 2 parts mint, 1 part lemon thyme

Herbs for Desserts

2 parts lemon balm, 1 part lemon thyme, 1 part angelica leaf

RIGHT: Roast Chicken Rub

HERBAL WINES

You can make delicious, medicated wines which act as tonics, digestive aids, sedatives and breath sweeteners as well as tasting good. In fact, by choosing your herbs you can devise wines for many different complaints. Be adventurous!

If you want a really mellow wine, let it mature for a month or so after straining. Store in a cool, dark place. If you want your wine to last a long time, it's best to choose a full-bodied wine as a base. For tonics I use a good muscat, as the flavour seems to blend well with herbs.

Honey Syrup for Liqueurs

Mix together equal quantities of water and honey, bring slowly to a boil, remove from the heat and stir until the honey is melted. Cool.

Honey syrup is suitable for adding to any drink which has a spirit base, such as whisky, brandy or vodka. If you add honey syrup, the liqueur needs to be matured for a further 2–3 months at room temperature.

Calming and Digestive Wine

This simple, effective recipe has been around since the turn of the century. Sip a glass to calm you down after a stressful day.

1 tablespoon chopped rosemary leaves
4 cloves
1 tablespoon honey
2.5cm (1in) piece cinnamon stick
1 bottle dry white wine

Place the herbs, cloves, honey and cinnamon into a sterilised bottle and top up with wine from a clean measuring jug. Shake daily until the honey is dissolved, then strain well. Drink after a week.

Tonic Wine

This wine is great any time you feel under·the weather or down in the mouth! It is a good pick-me-up after illness to stimulate the appetite, or can be drunk just because you like it. Use fresh herbs if you can get them for this wine and bruise them (don't completely crush them) one at a time by pounding gently two or three times in a mortar and pestle.

1 teaspoon each wormwood, rosemary, thyme and sage
2cm (^{3}/4in) piece fresh ginger
2cm (^{3}/4in) piece cinnamon stick
3 whole cloves
peel of 1 lemon, pared thinly and sliced
2 teaspoons aniseed
2 cups (500ml/16fl oz) muscat

Place the herbs and spices into a sterilised bottle and top up with the wine (the measuring jug must be very clean). Cork and store in a cool, dark place for 2 weeks.

Strain and filter the wine and pour back into the bottle. Leave in a cool dark place for 1 month before use. Sweeten with Honey Syrup if you like.

Digestive Liqueur

1 tablespoon each crushed caraway seed and fennel seed
2cm (^{3}/4in) piece fresh ginger, crushed
1 tablespoon chopped peppermint leaves
2 strips lemon peel, about 5cm (2in) each
2 cups (500ml/16fl oz) brandy
^{1}/2 cup (125ml/4fl oz) Honey Syrup

Combine all the ingredients and stand in a cool place for 3–4 weeks. Strain and filter, then stand 3 months in a cool, dark place before drinking.

RIGHT: From left: Mint Liqueur (on page 250), Calming and Digestive Wine

Mint Liqueur

2 tablespoons peppermint leaves, bruised

2 tablespoons spearmint leaves, bruised

4 strips orange peel, each about 5cm (2in)

4 strips lemon peel, each about 5cm (2in)

2$^1/_2$ cups (625ml/20fl oz) brandy

$^1/_2$ cup (125ml/4fl oz) Honey Syrup

Place the herbs, peels and brandy in a large sterilised jar. Shake once daily for 2 weeks. Strain and filter.

Add the Honey Syrup, then bottle and store in a dark, cool place for 2–3 months.

Mint Liqueur

SPROUTING SEEDS

Sprouting seeds and grains is a way of growing fresh greens, even if you live in a one-room apartment. Sprouts are full of vitamins and minerals. They taste good and are cheap, easy and fun to grow. Even if you have a large garden it's not practical to grow some herbs outside, notably alfalfa, red clover, mung, lentils and fenugreek. The alternative is to sprout the seeds and use the sprouts, either dried or fresh, in many ways – including for food.

A word of warning before you begin. Seeds bought from a farm or garden supplier have most likely been sprayed to protect them from insect attack. These sprays are most poisonous and the seeds shouldn't be used. Get your supplies from a health food shop or a supplier who can guarantee the seeds and grains haven't been treated in any way.

It's always a temptation to sprout too much seed when you first begin. The seeds look so small that it's impossible to imagine the size they will grow to. As a guide to quantities, remember that $^1/_4$ cup of seeds becomes 2 cups of sprouts, and it's better to maintain a steady supply of fresh sprouts than to have bowls full of sprouts losing goodness in the refrigerator.

It isn't necessary to buy expensive equipment to do your sprouting. Chances are that you already have everything you need in your home.

CONTAINERS FOR SPROUTING

All sorts of containers can be used for sprouting. Look around your house and you will find many things that can be used: colanders, sink tidies, sieves, tea strainers (sprouts for one person!) or some of the ideas following.

UNGLAZED FLOWERPOT SAUCERS

These are inexpensive, easily available, aesthetically pleasing to have around the kitchen and they work well. Different sizes allow for different-sized sprouts. You will need two of each size at a time.

Wash and soak the containers in water to prepare them before starting the sprouting. Sprinkle the soaked and drained seeds evenly in the bottom of one saucer and invert the other saucer to cover it. Stand them in a dish of water, which will be absorbed through the unglazed saucers. Keep them near the stove or in a kitchen cupboard. Another good place is on top of the refrigerator towards the back, where the heat escapes. Top up the dish of water as needed.

When the plants are as tall as you want, take the top saucer off, leave them standing in the container of water and put them near a window for a day or so. They will grow a little more during this time and develop their green leaves. Store in a cool, dark place or in the refrigerator.

ICE CREAM CONTAINERS

Square or round 2 litre ($3^1/2$ pint) ice cream containers make excellent sprouting trays. They don't look pretty, but they don't cost anything and are very efficient. To prepare them, punch a lot of holes in the bottom with a skewer. I use these for big seeds like mung beans, lentils and fenugreek, but you can make them suitable for small seed by laying blotting paper, cheesecloth or nylon fly netting in the base. Spread the soaked and strained seeds evenly over the bottom of the container and put the lid on. Twice a day stand the container in enough water to come up through the holes and just cover the seeds, then lift it out and let it drain. Then treat it in the same way as described for saucers.

GLASS JARS

Any sized glass jar can be used. You will need some sort of cover for the jar to allow air to circulate among the sprouts inside the jar, or they will rot. A piece of nylon fly netting, coarse cheesecloth, net curtaining or old pantihose will do, with an elastic band to hold the cover on. Remember the eventual size of the plants, for it becomes difficult to rinse them properly if they are too closely packed. Keeping the jar on its side, grow the sprouts in the same way as described, rinsing them daily. To keep out as much light as possible, cover all but the mouth with a folded cloth or place in a cupboard.

HOW TO SPROUT SEEDS

First, remove any debris or broken seeds before you begin sprouting. If these bits are left in, they may rot and spoil the whole batch.

Rinse the seeds and soak in warm water overnight. Drain, pouring the drained water on indoor plants or using it for stock in cooking. Put the seeds in your chosen container and keep them moist (not wet), in dark and warm conditions. They need rinsing each day or they will begin to rot or dry out.

When alfalfa and red clover sprouts are about 2cm ($^3/4$in) long and the little leaves appear (after 3–5 days), they can be exposed to sunlight for a time until the leaves turn green. Mung, lentils and fenugreek can be eaten as soon as the roots are 7mm ($^1/4$in) long. Don't leave them too long or they will become bitter. When ready, take them out of the sprouting container, rinse well and put them in a covered dish in the refrigerator or other very cool place. Try to use within 4–5 days (rinsing each day) to gain the maximum goodness.

GUIDE TO MEASURES

As the enjoyment of good home-made food and the love of cooking spreads throughout the world, it's important to have easy-to-follow conversion of measures in our recipes. In some countries they use metric measures, in others imperial measures, and many cooks like to use handy cup and spoon measures. In Australia, we use metric measures and cup and spoon measures approved by the Standards Association of Australia.

- The metric measuring cup holds 250ml
- The metric measuring tablespoon holds 20ml
- The metric measuring teaspoon holds 5ml

The conversions given in the recipes in this book are approximate. Any differences should not make any noticeable difference to these recipes.

We use 60g (2oz) eggs in our recipes.

Dry Measures		Liquid Measures		Helpful Measures	
METRIC	IMPERIAL	METRIC	IMPERIAL	METRIC	IMPERIAL
15g	½ oz	30ml	1 fluid oz	3mm	⅛ in
30g	1oz	60ml	2 fluid oz	6mm	¼ in
60g	2oz	100ml	3 fluid oz	1cm	½ in
90g	3oz	125ml	4 fluid oz	2cm	¾ in
100g	3½oz	150ml	5 fluid oz	2.5cm	1in
125g	4oz (¼lb)		(¼ pint/1 gill)	5cm	2in
155g	5oz	185ml	6 fluid oz	6cm	2½ in
185g	6oz	250ml	8 fluid oz	8cm	3in
200g	6½oz	300ml	10 fluid oz (½ pint)	10cm	4in
220g	7oz	500ml	16 fluid oz	13cm	5in
250g	8oz (½lb)	750ml	24 fluid oz	15cm	6in
280g	9oz	1000ml (1 litre)	32 fluid oz	18cm	7in
315g	10oz		(1¾ pints)	20cm	8in
345g	11oz			23cm	9in
375g	12oz (¾lb)			25cm	10in
410g	13oz			28cm	11in
440g	14oz			30cm	12in (1ft)
470g	15oz				
500g	16oz (1lb)				
750g	24oz (1½lb)				
1kg	32oz (2lb)				

Oven Temperatures

These oven temperatures are only a guide. Always check the manufacturer's manual.

	C (CELSIUS)	F (FAHRENHEIT)	GAS MARK
VERY SLOW	120	250	1
SLOW	150	300	2
MODERATELY SLOW	160	325	3
MODERATE	180	350	4
MODERATELY HOT	190	375	5
HOT	200	400	6
VERY HOT	230	450	7

INDEX

Credits

Herb Gardens, Butterfly Photography: Virginia
Wallace-Crabbe
Extra Herb and Herb Garden Shots Supplied by
the Diggers Club, Dromana, Victoria
Step-by-step Herb Photography: Ivy Hansen
Food Styling: Karen Cotton
Lifestyle Styling: Donna Hoyle, Louise Owens
Flower Arrangements and Floral Border by
Angie Summers,
Summers Floral, Woollahra, NSW

Editors: Jan Castorina, Lesley Wickham
Designer: Anna Soo
Designer's Assistant: Raylee Sloane
Editorial Assistants: Ella Martin,
Carolyn Uyeda
Technical Assistance: Pamela Allardice
Stylist's Assistant: Liz Nolan

Acknowledgements

There are many people who have been an invaluable help to me during the writing of this book. I have received information, advice, support and tolerance (the last very important during my many 'nervous' days). I give my love and thanks to Prakash, my husband, for all the years together; Nirala, someone very special, who was with me during all the farm adventures and who can always be relied upon; Fred Kraeter, a fount of knowledge, willingly shared, of all things pharmaceutical; Priya and Tony Martin, dear friends who carefully, and with humour, proofread the manuscript; Norm, my son-in-law, who compiled lists of gardening equipment and listened to my moans; Jane, my lovely daughter, who tested a lot of the skin care formulae even when she didn't have much time; Satyamo, a sensitive photographer and a good friend; my children who have survived my whims and grown into wonderful people; my editor, Jan Castorina; and to all herbalists throughout the ages without whose courage and persistence none of us would have the knowledge we have today.